Forrest Park Publishers
Bellingham • Washington

First Edition

Copyright © 1999 by Daniel Homel

FORREST PARK PUBLISHERS
P.O. Box 29775
Bellingham, Washington 98228
(360) 647-2505

PRINTED IN THE UNITED STATES OF AMERICA

ISBN: 1-879522-14-4

Contents

Early American Fly Reels 5
(1874 - 1930)

Later American Fly Reels 51
(1930 - 1975)

Great Britain Fly Reels 85
(Europe)

Automatic Fly Reels 123
(Spring Loaded)

Fly Reel Value Guide 143

Credits

Photography — D.B. Homel **PMT** — Quicksilver Lab

Electronic Pre-Press — Cindy Szankiewicz

Frontis — *Thomas Chubb 1883 folding reel foot patent*

The following list represents those who generously contributed reels to be photographed during the compilation process: Harold Jellison, Dave Mair, Mike Berry, Dick Van Demark, and Walt Johnson. Thank you, my friends.

On the cover — Antique salmon flies, a *Bunyan Bug*, Marathon *Bass-Houn*, Tuttle's *Devil Bug*, South Bend *Hop-Oreno*, along with two reproductions tied by the author and Dr. Dan Coombs.

Early American Fly Reels
(1874 - 1930)

Precursors and Archetypes

The traditional single action fly reel, as we know it, can be said to have evolved from the simple brass winches and pirns of 18th century Britain. Post colonial sport fishing enthusiasts in the eastern United States relied heavily on angling equipment imported from England and Scotland. In *American Angler's Book* (1864), Thadeus Norris, a learned outdoorsman, dispensed a bit of tackle advice when he recommended the ultimate reel for North American trout fishing:

> " . . . one with a short axle, which brings the plates of the reel close together . . . as it winds the line more compactly on the spool."

Norris, like most anglers of this period, was not a fly purist but a generalist and his simple reel of choice was a tiny two inch diameter Birmingham crank model from England. It is clear, however, that the true American fly fishing reel has a portion of Yankee roots. To find its origin, one need only look at two particularly unusual early American reels — The **Billinghurst** and The **Fowler Gem**.

William Billinghurst of Rochester, New York was granted a patent for his "Fishing Line Reel" on August 9, 1859. Billinghurst's invention represents what many consider to be our first glimpse at the American fly reel. It is evident from the patent application that the inventor did not specifically intend the reel be for fly fishing. In fact Billinghurst's patent text relates to improvements over bait casting reels of the time. Nevertheless, he does mention the term "skeleton" in reference to the conformation of his reel's cage-like spool which consisted of inter-connected metal rings. This most certainly is the earliest documentation of the ventilated skeleton reel style, a construction that would influence the basic design of many fly reels

6

to follow. From Billinghurst's writings and dictum can be gleaned the benefit of a ventilated reel:

" . . . but the great advantage consists in the complete exposure of the line, whereby it is enabled to dry rapidly and thoroughly . . . in my improved reel there is but a small portion of the line covered, and the whole surface is fully exposed to the air."

Although the principle of line ventilation is apparent in Billinghurst's work of 1859, we now realize that the structure of his reel more closely resembles the Indiana style casting reels of the 1930s which were side-mounted to the rod (the Heddon-Boyer Winona, Kiest, and Goite reels). Regardless of the fact that Billinghurst invented less than a pure fly reel, his creation was a monumental step away from the heavy brass multiplying reels prevalent in the United States prior to the Civil War.

In 1872, Dr. Alonzo Fowler of Batavia, New York patented a simple perforated-spool reel made of Vulcanite (hard rubber). Fowler used the term "skeleton" to describe his reel spool, though its structure consisted merely of drilled-out round holes — a pattern far less complex than the Billinghurst rings arrangement. Unlike The Billinghurst, Dr. Fowler's reel was at least promoted as being appropriate for fly fishing. The lightweight Fowler reel, known by the trade name *Gem*, would provide a reasonable degree of balance when placed at the butt end of a fly rod. But alas, here was still another reel that was designed to be mounted horizontally on the rod. Perhaps this is why a subsequent invention, The Orvis Reel, stands-out as the first authentic, commercially produced American fly reel.

Charles F. Orvis, a pioneer angling innovator and mail order entrepreneur, began his tackle business in 1856. Orvis, who resided in Vermont, is deemed to be the inventor of the famous glass minnow trap and was an early maker of bamboo rods. A patent application for his ingenious click reel was filed on April 4, 1874. Legal rights to the design were perfected on May 12, 1874 in Letters Patent No. 150,883.

The patent text is curious in that it begins to describe a reel constructed of perforated <u>hard rubber</u> disks. And the accompanying patent drawing clearly diagrams a combination of hard rubber and metal parts. Orvis was obviously toying with the idea of fabricating the reel in this manner. When the actual production took place, however, nickel plated metal was used exclusively (with the exception of a wood winding knob). Orvis had left his options open when he alluded to this alternative form of construction near the end of the patent document:

> "I have described the above reel in which the perforated disks are made of hard rubber; but do not wish to be confined to this material, as the reel may be made of metal throughout."

It would seem that for purposes of durability, Orvis decided to proceed with the metal version. In any case, he created what is now the classic American fly reel antique. It had many of the primary attributes deemed necessary by fly fishers of 1874 and today — including generous spool and frame perforations for lightness and ventilation. The extremely narrow configuration of the spool allowed for rapid line take-up.

Orvis' new reel was considered to be versatile, and was not sold to fly casters alone. Yes indeed a good number were put into service for the purpose of dangling nightcrawlers. In setting the record straight, catalog pages from 1882 illustrate the reel affixed to a fly rod, below the hand grip and in a position underneath the reel seat and grip. Reference is also made to yardage capacity in relation to fly lines. Finally, a genuine American fly reel with a distinct identity was born!

The first issue of The Orvis Reel was fastened together with rivets and sold for $5.00 nestled in a black walnut case. Just a few years later the price had come down to $3.50 — with a wide spool model for bass fishing at $4.00 including the case. The idea of a suitable carrying box is actually addressed in the original Orvis patent, although wood as a material is not mentioned. The case, which had a special slot tailored to fit the removable crank and knob, was intended to allow a convenient means for transporting the reel safely in a coat pocket. Today, collectible value is greatly enhanced if a reel is found in its original walnut case.

By 1905 The Orvis Reel had been improved with the introduction of screws in-place of rivets. A removable oil cap was also added to the reel back plate. The influence of mass production, and elimination of the walnut case, initiated another price reduction. Both nickel plated and aluminum versions were available at this time and into the next decade direct from Orvis or through authorized dealers.

The Raised Pillar Reel

Either by furtive response to Orvis' idea, or by sheer act of independent ingenuity, two craftsmen from Bangor, Maine developed a then novel frame design that would inspire the shape of a plethora of reels to follow. The *Philbrook and Payne* raised pillar reel was introduced by a patent of June 12, 1877 at which time it was simultaneously assigned to Hiram Leonard (patriarch of the American bamboo rod industry). The patent application is in the name of Francis Philbrook alone, although most of the initial reels are known to have been machined by Edward F. Payne, a one-time

Leonard employee and master cane rod builder. The pivotal characteristic of Philbrook's reel is the appearance of five "nubs" or off-sets spaced at consistent intervals on the front and back plates which cause the cross-bars (pillars) to be raised-up. With the pillars raised clear away from the spool and reel foot, greater practical line capacity was achieved. The result was a compact and strong reel capable of carrying a surprising length of fly line in proportion to its size and weight.

The rudimentary Philbrook invention was marketed as the **Leonard Click Reel** for nearly a century, yet a few pre-1877 Philbrook and Payne prototype reels do exist in collections. These are phenomenally rare reels exhibiting marbled hard rubber plates and engraved with the words "Philbrook & Payne, Makers — Pat. Apld. For".

Several cosmetic variations of the Philbrook & Payne reel soon developed under the Leonard name. The foremost examples sought-after by antiquarians are the Leonard all-metal trout reel (marked "H.L. Leonard, Pat. June 12, 1877") and Leonard silver/hard rubber trout reel (marked "H.L. Leonard Pat. No. 191813"). Many of these diminutive 2 1/4 to 3 inch trout reels were sold by Leonard's agent **William Mills & Son** of New York. Later reels are marked "Leonard-Mills" indicating a time when Mills had absorbed the Leonard firm. It is also interesting to note that Edward Payne produced a similar reel called *The Kosmic Fly Casting Reel* in 1895. And the design was not limited to trout reels as evidenced by numerous salmon or grilse sizes found in tackle collections.

The New York makers Conroy, Malleson, and Julius Vom Hofe all produced raised pillar fly reels during a time when the Leonard reel was gaining prominence. Many of these reels had a comparable appearance to Philbrook's design with the predominant feature of hard rubber plates encircled by reinforcing bands and off-sets of nickel-silver. Delicate Half-handles or full, counter-balanced cranks were combined with black ebonite or white knobs. Both the **Conroy** company and **Julius Vom Hofe** supplied reels to tackle retailers and distributors such as Abbey & Imbrie, Dame Stoddard, William Read & Sons, Mills, Orvis, and A.G. Spalding Brothers.

A Consummate Reel Maker

Julius Vom Hofe might be considered one of the best fly reel makers ever. Borrowing a phrase from boxing, Edward Vom Hofe might have been the greatest of all time.

Julius and Edward were the sons of reel craftsman Frederich Vom Hofe and, like their father, created quality reels both in terms of form and function. Several competing Vom Hofe big game trolling reels (Julius B-Ocean and Edward 621 series) were allied in characteristics and now warrant similar values on the collectible market. With regard to their fly reels, the close similarities begin to fade.

Edward Vom Hofe embarked on a journey of invention that would lead to such landmark reel features as the basic click tension device (1883 patent) which has since been liberally imitated and incorporated into millions of reels worldwide. But it is for a particular series of high-end fly reels that his New York company is best remembered by ardent tackle collectors.

Unlike the simple Julius Vom Hofe raised pillar reels fashioned after Philbrook's patent, Edward Vom Hofe specialized in building elegant hard rubber trout and salmon fly reels with recessed pillars, trimmed in highly polished silver components. One smaller model, the *Perfection* (#360) trout reel, was equipped with a sophisticated, adjustable check mechanism and movable oiling cap. No mere click reels were these!

Large salmon fly reels such as the *Restigouche* (#423) and the multiplying *Tobique* (#504) came fitted with a unique tension drag patented by Edward Charles Vom Hofe on July 14, 1896. Generally speaking, for the drag to operate, a set of spider-like arms make contact against a disk causing smooth tension when the line is played-out from the reel. Upon retrieve, the arms are automatically disengaged and tension is eliminated. The tension can be adjusted by means of a silver dial on the back plate which points to designated settings. Impeccable antique reels of this stature rival anything we produced today — so naturally Vom Hofes are now outrageously expensive to acquire.

The Edward Vom Hofe reel making tradition was perpetuated into the 1940s by a shop foreman, Otto Zwarg. Zwarg produced identical salmon models under his own name using Vom Hofe tooling and parts. The Zwarg operation was housed in St. Petersburg, Florida.

Skeleton Fly Reels

The skeleton designation can apply not only to the open, perforated structure of a fly reel frame and spool, but to the "bare bones", no-nonsense function of such a simple device. Notice, I did not say <u>cheap</u> device. It is a fact, however, that most skeleton style fly reels were <u>very inexpensive</u>. Advertising from the 1902 Sears Catalog tells us that single action skeleton trout reels (attributed to Meisselbach) sold for $1.36 plus 10 cents postage. Sears did sell a tiny, raised pillar reel made of solid brass for 15¢ — now that's cheap.

August F. Meisselbach is without question the king of skeleton fly reel makers. Teamed with his brother William in Newark, New Jersey, Meisselbach launched one of the truly prolific reel assembling operations in America. Their first effort in 1886 was a side-mounted, frameless trolling reel known as the *Amateur*.

The Meisselbach brothers' most significant contribution to the development of the skeleton fly reel design stems from their patent of February 5, 1889. It was in this document that they described, by means of crisp drawings and careful text, a method for applying pressure from reel frame to spool resulting in the creation of drag. The design was manifest in the *Expert* series of single action reels. The key ingredient to this invention was a yielding spring-steel frame that encircled the spool. Drag or friction could be engaged when the angler pressed thumb or finger against the flexible frame, which in turn caused the frame to rub against the spool — slowing its rotation.

Seven years later, the Meisselbachs offered a reel combining a raised pillar, ventilated frame and a skeleton spool. This was, of course, the beginning of the Meisselbach *Featherlight* fly reel. The new reel bore an improved click mechanism. The improved click is revealed to us in Patent No. 553,069 dated January 14, 1896. To prolong the useful life of the reel click, Meisselbach installed a double-headed pawl which could be reversed if one end wore out. Upon removal of a single screw and tension spring, the pawl could be conveniently turned-around by the consumer — thus a costly factory repair was avoided.

The Featherlight was eventually reissued in a purely skeleton form which was based on a later patent of December 27, 1904. Meisselbach fly reels, like the Featherlight, are invariably stamped with the date corresponding to a particular patent. These markings should be scrutinized by the collector, since they allow for easy identification if other engraved data is obliterated. The 1904 Featherlight resembles a "low fat" version of the Expert series and was sold by the dozen, in several diameter sizes, to retailers throughout the country.

One of the more difficult early Meisselbach single action reels to locate is the *Allright*. The Allright sold in the same price range as the Expert, and bears a resemblance to it with the exception of a solid back on the frame <u>and</u> spool. Clearly, the Allright would be suitable for fly fishing — yet in 1905 it was advertised by William Mills & Son exclusively as a bass casting or trolling reel. From various patent illustrations depicting a position "on top of the rod", we are able to deduce that any of the classic Meisselbach fly reels could have been intended to serve a dual purpose.

Quite a few other firms produced skeleton style fly reels. Not to be forgotten are the substantial *Ideal* and *Gem* from the **Rochester Reel Company** of New York. The fine Ideal fly reels were available in solid German silver, while the side-mounted Gem could be purchased in an alternative nickel-plated brass. For the angler-collector seeking traditional charm and function, it is the Ideal that is the most desirable of the two.

The Ideal came in two sizes, the No. 1 for trout and No. 2 for bass. At the core of the Ideal series was a very complex lever operated drag arrangement patented in 1910. Three settings allowed for tension, free-spool, and click. An elaborate layering of tiny metal parts coordinated with the lever and a brass tension plate to facilitate the multi-faceted operation. The integrated steel click was poised for action by a small spring that is often missing. Having been built with a German silver frame and spool, the Ideal is rigid and heavy compared to most skeleton reels. This highly collectible fly reel can develop a beautiful light tarnish and lovely antique patina — making it very attractive as a display piece.

Another exceptional skeleton style reel collectible is the **Carlton** Manufacturing Company *Lightweight*. This little jewel is scarce when compared to the prodigious number of Meisselbach fly reels found in collections. What sets the Carlton Lightweight apart from other skeleton reels is the complete encapsulation of its spool within a perforated frame. Moreover, the Carlton can be easily and quickly disassembled without tools by means of a unique pillar to frame connection.

Enterprise Mfg. Company

The Ohio based Enterprise Manufacturing Company, with products circulated under the trade names Portage, Four Brothers, and Pflueger, can be traced back to a start-up date of 1864. Pflueger is often referred to as the "bulldog" brand since the familiar bow-legged-canine logo was prominently engraved on a multitude of reel feet. Early company history portrays this entity as an active distributor and importer of trolling spoons, silk minnows, flies, hooks, and hand lines.

At first, **Pflueger** sold a variety of single action reels of the kind produced by Julius Vom Hofe. From 1895 forward, they began to formulate proprietary designs outlined in a number of patents. Earnest Pflueger's patent No. 560,925 (1896) describes a wood hand-held fishing reel with a single winding knob and integrated tension lever. Specimens with two knobs also exist. Although his intriguing wood reel was not a fly reel, excerpts of patent text express the high value Mr. Pflueger placed on line ventilation. Maybe this hand held model was some sort of eccentric forerunner to the skeleton style Pflueger *Progress* and *Sal-Trout* fly reels.

Pflueger's Progress rivals any early fly reel on a scale of longevity or quantity sold. "Bulldog Progress" is a nick-name assigned by collectors to signify the early skeleton Progress reel as opposed to second generation contemporary models. The Progress was stocked by a battalion of Pflueger dealers and was especially popular with anglers just before and after World War One. It was offered in several finishes including nickel-plating over brass and a deep gun-metal or blued-brass. South Bend Bait Company of Indiana marketed a similar skeleton fly reel called the *St. Joe*, while Shakespeare sold the almost identical *Kazoo*. Either of these is a tougher find than the more common Progress.

The Sal-Trout was a much heftier appliance often touted as a trolling reel. First issue of the Sal-Trout was all-brass and it makes an outstanding "wall hanger" when combined with a long bamboo or lancewood rod.

Aiming to supply the more sophisticated angler, Pflueger had some top notch fly reels in its quiver. In 1903, Joseph E. Pflueger patented a process in which a thin sheet of metal could be laminated between two disks of vulcanized rubber to create a reel side-plate of superior strength and resiliency. This type of side-plate is called a "sandwich" in the collector vernacular. The diagram in his patent application shows a casting reel, however the sandwich side-plate concept was later applied to Pflueger's *Golden West* fly reel (circa 1925). The Golden West is a must-have item for Pflueger aficionados.

Another single action trout reel from the same era, the *Hawkeye*, is a prime Pflueger collectible. The Hawkeye frame was constructed of hard rubber with nickel-silver encircling bands. It did not have the patented sandwich side-plates. The Four Brothers *Delite* is a close cousin to the Hawkeye.

Strangely more difficult to locate than the Golden West, Hawkeye, or Delite is the Four Brothers *Egalite*. The Egalite is known to have been produced both in a counter-balance single knob model and interesting twin knob version. This was a nice, no-frills, light click reel complete with recessed aluminum front plate. Try to find one today — it ain't easy!

Trade Reels

Collectors, dealers, and appraisers are occasionally stumped when attempting to identify small brass or nickel antique trout reels. As the hobby of fishing tackle collecting has moved from its infancy of the 1960s toward recognition as a legitimate (and often quite profitable) segment of the antique trade, the level of sophistication and knowledge among dealers has increased. Nevertheless, the typical comment reserved for identifying unmarked little crank reels has not changed much — "it's a Hendryx". In many cases the observation that Hendryx was the maker would be correct simply because the odds favor it. And this fact cannot be ignored — Hendryx produced a ton of no-name "trade reels".

Hendryx patent history remains the single most effective research tool that can be put to use in identifying many of these neat little reels. As a preface to Hendryx patent dating and chronology it is interesting to know something about the manufacturer. The Andrew B. Hendryx Company of New Haven, Connecticut was set-up in 1879 to produce bird-cages, wire, and other items involving metal fabrication. The existence of Hendryx brand steel cat beds indicates that the pet trade was an important part of the business.

On October 26, 1886 the company founder, Andrew Hendryx, was granted his first fishing reel patent (a level wind mechanism). This date marks the firm's diversification into fishing reels, although an earlier wire-fastening patent of 1876 is often stamped on Hendryx reel feet. Subsequent Hendryx fishing reel patent dates include:

July 10, 1888
Reinforcing collars for the center of a reel spool

September 15, 1891
Automatic free-spool clutch disengaged upon retrieve

April 26, 1892
Improved spool bearing

July 5, 1892
Efficient production technique for reel gearing

December 6, 1892
Optional external ring allowing for economical production of two different reel styles

April 6, 1897
Convenient lubrication cap on head plate

July 29, 1902
Integrated washer under handle prevents dirt from invading the internal mechanism of reel

February 7, 1905
Means of securing a cover disk to recessed reel plates

Of course, not all of these patents relate to fly reels. And often times the name "Hendryx" is found emblazoned across a reel foot along with the familiar 1876 and 1888 patent dates for no-brainer identification. In any case, the foregoing data demonstrates the diversity and inventiveness of a prolific reel maker (Hendryx output prior to the turn of the century is estimated at two million reels).

The fishing tackle division of Hendryx was sold to Winchester Repeating Arms Company in 1919. Small, attractive **Winchester** fly reels have become extremely popular as a result of the "crossover" collecting phenomena. Winchester gun and tool collectors, as well as general fly reel collectors, passionately pursue the little nickel-plated reels marked with a classic Winchester logo. *Armax* was also a Winchester brand name stamped prominently on both skeleton and solid spool models.

Hendryx was not the only purveyor of trade reels. Pflueger, Pennel, and Chubb were others. By all accounts, **Thomas Chubb** represented the exemplar of a rugged American work ethic. Early in

1869 he established a humble fishing tackle factory at Post Mills, Vermont. But October floods of the same year swept away his shop and all its contents resulting in a loss of $28,000. He quickly erected another building upon the same site — though a second misfortune loomed on the horizon. The plant was consumed by fire in 1875. Undaunted, Mr. Chubb soon rebuilt to a substantial size of 15,000 square feet.

Thomas Chubb was best known as a builder of economy wood fly rods. Appropriately, one of his inventions relates to a reel foot — the part that mates with the rod. *The Chubb Fishing Reel*, patented on July 31, 1883, features a folding reel foot independently pivoted to the side plates. Chubb reasoned that this contrivance would obviate the awkward shape of the reel and allow it to fit in a round case. A more important part of the Chubb reel was a simple and effective permanent click device operated by a spring and pawl meshing smoothly with a toothed wheel — all mounted internally to the back plate.

While many Pflueger brass crank reels were clearly marked, most Chubbs were not. A rough identification rule of thumb to follow would be to look at the thickness of the brass. The Chubb tends to be noticeably stout and heavy when compared to the average Pflueger, or Hendryx for that matter.

To make things more confusing, all of these major reel producers sold private label models to their retail dealers and wholesale distributors. For example, early *Abbey & Imbrie* reels were made for them trade-marked with two hooks in a heart shape. Talk about variations, there were literally thousands of 'em. And despite the decent value these cool antiques hold today — they were nearly a dime-a-dozen (or a dime each) back in the late 1890s. The typical catalog price for a tiny brass trade reel with no click was under $1.50 per <u>dozen</u> or about 12¢ each!

The Rare and Mysterious

Two special early fly reels stand-out as examples of what a collector might unexpectedly find hidden in an old attic or barn loft. They are mentioned purposefully to pique the reader's interest and muster some enthusiasm. Too often, devoted collectors give-up searching due to competition from intense garage sale junkies or the pressure placed on their hobby by the growing investment potential of old fishing tackle. Indeed, astute financial advisers now recommend that a diversified portfolio include a small percentage of antiques. All of this publicity makes it nearly impossible to ferret-out good stuff for your collection at a fair and reasonable price. Nevertheless, rare items appear out-of-the-blue regularly. If you keep looking, one of the following may turn-up.

The Talbot *Ben Hur* is an immensely valuable fly reel antique. It appeared in limited quantities circa 1905. The Ben Hur was available crafted completely in German silver (most desirable) or with aluminum plates, a silver foot and silver crossbars. The reel was cataloged in two line capacities at a size of approximately 2 1/2 inches in diameter. Price was ten dollars. William Talbot gained fame as a designer of "Kentucky style" multiplying reels, although his factory was located in Missouri. The monetary worth of his renown bait casters Comet, Mars, and Meteor now pales in comparison to the Ben Hur fly reel.

A reel we know little about is the *Kewart*, produced by Chas. H. Kewell Co. of San Francisco, California. It was available circa 1918 in 3 inch and 3 1/4 inch sizes. Price was $10 and $12 respectively. Kewarts have a black finish, cast aluminum frame and spool coupled with a brass reel foot. This scarce reel features a unique drag composed of a tightly coiled spring soldered to the spool shaft (axle). The axle has been cast in one piece with the main reel frame. As the drag fitting on the spool face is tightened, the coiled spring expands — forcing a brass ratchet against a click pawl mounted on the back plate. Having dissected an actual specimen of this reel, it is easy to see why the design did not endure. You might say it was functionally obsolete on the day it was made. Sure, the durability of the Kewart fly reel is questionable, yet encounters with it are infrequent. The combination of these factors equates to a splendid collectible!

Leonard trout reel loaded with a new weight-forward fly line. Notice the great capacity achieved by virtue of the raised pillar design.

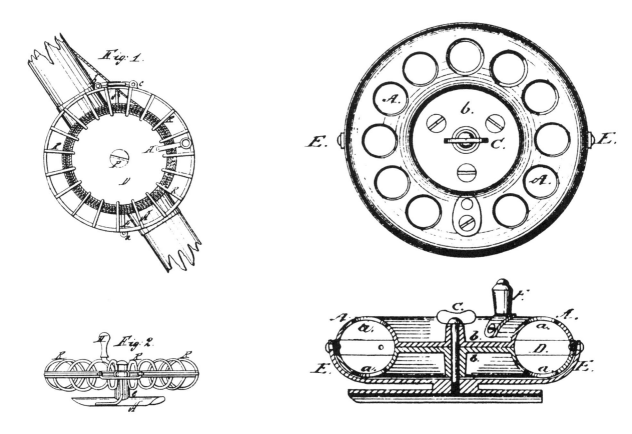

Left: The *William Billinghurst Reel* as shown in an original patent drawing of 1859. The design not only provided for spool ventilation but also rapid line take-up which enabled the maker to dispense with more complicated and expensive gearing usually required for that purpose. The Billinghurst Reel retrieved more than seven inches of line with one revolution — nearly ten times the efficiency of a common crank reel. Figure 1 represents the reel as it sits upon a rod. Figure 2 is a side elevation of the reel which clearly displays a series of interconnected, divided rings through which the line is coiled. **Right:** 1877 patent drawing of the *Fowler Gem*. Crux of the invention, according to Fowler, is the non-corrosive nature of its vulcanite frame.

A classic *C.F. Orvis* 1874 fly reel measuring 2 3/4″ in diameter and constructed of nickel-plated brass with a wood crank knob.

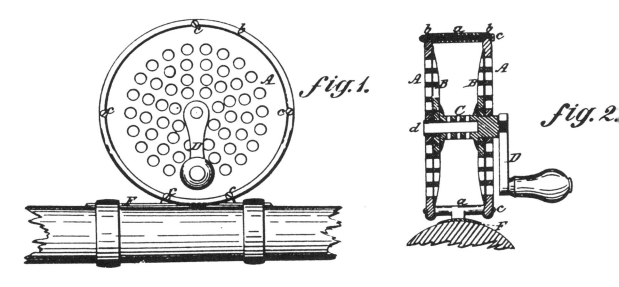

Inventor:

Charles F. Orvis.

Patent drawing of the Orvis reel dated May 12, 1874. In the document text, Charles Orvis expounds upon the theory behind his ventilated fly reel: *In winding up the wet line, the water escapes through the perforations in the disks (**parts A and B**) and in the hollow shaft, out through its open end (**part d**), and when wound-up . . . a current of air is continually forcing itself through the line, and all mildew and rot thereby avoided, as under these circumstances the line soon becomes thoroughly dried.*

24

Tail plate of an Orvis 1874 fly reel reveals a cap that can be removed for cleaning and lubrication. A layout of five screws is utilized to retain the crossbars and reel foot. Engraved with the words *Orvis Maker — Patented Manchester, VT.*

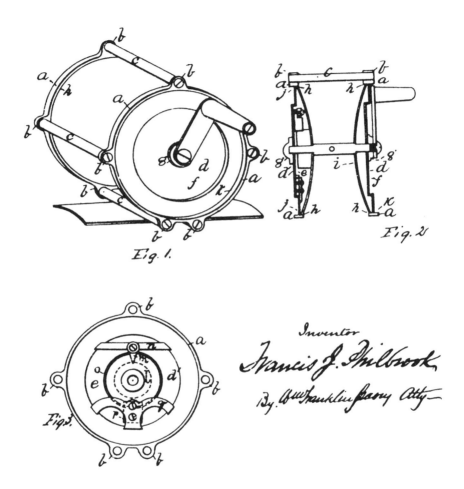

Fig. 1.

Fig. 2.

Fig. 3.

Inventor
Francis J. Philbrook
By. Wm Franklin Seavy Atty—

The Francis Philbrook patent of 1877 assigned to Hiram Leonard of Bangor, Maine. This famous raised pillar design has its inception in the dictum of Philbrook's short patent summary: *My reel is constructed with an annular frame* (**part a**), *provided with offsets* (**parts b**), *through which pass the crossbars* (**parts c**), *which unite the sides of the reel with each other.* Figure 3 shows a simple click ratchet and dog (pawl) operated by a wire spring (**part o**). These pieces were secured in-place by screws to allow for easy removal for repairs.

A Leonard-Mills raised pillar reel following the design of Philbrook's patent (circa 1905). Constructed with hard rubber plates and aluminum rims with a nickel-silver handle and foot. A knurled drag adjuster and movable oil cover are found on the tail plate marked *Light ~ Heavy*.

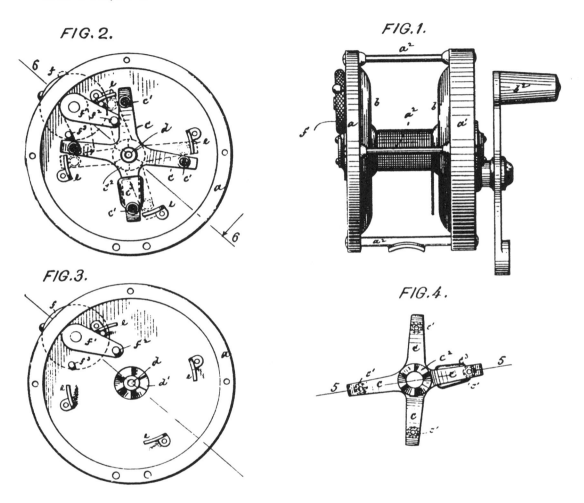

FIG. 2.   FIG.1.   FIG.3.   FIG.4.

The Edward Vom Hofe patent of 1896 as incorporated into his fine fly reels of the same era. The invention relates primarily to a tension device that consists of a resilient, slotted brake or *spider* (**part c**) which is set into the reel plate (**part a**). Tips of the bent, spider-like arms are provided with brake shoes that, when engaged, make contact with a disk on the inside surface of the reel spool. Upon line retrieval the brake shoes automatically recede from the disk a sufficient distance to relieve any tension.

Spectacular Edward Vom Hofe *Restigouche* #423 (6/0 size). Made of silver and hard rubber with a drag adjuster dial (clockwise lightens the tension). Red dots appear on the tail plate for drag setting. Bears the July 14, 1896 patent date.

A. F. & W. MEISSELBACH.
FISHING REEL.

No. 553,069.　　　　　　　　　Patented Jan. 14, 1896.

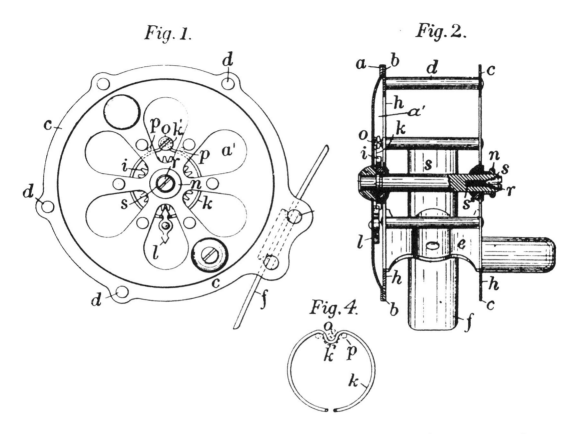

Fig. 1.

Fig. 2.

Fig. 4.

August and William Meisselbach's patent granted in 1896. It describes their solution to a problem found in similar reels of the time: *The pivot pin for the click . . . is in all cases riveted to prevent it from being jarred loose in the normal action of the click in engagement with its toothed wheel, and it is therefore impracticable to secure said click removably in place for convenient renewal. As such a member of the device receives the hardest wear and its renewal can be attended only with considerable expense and with the inconvenience of its return to the manufacturer for such purpose, we have devised the double headed click* (**part l**), *which may be readily reversed so as to double the life of such member by the mere removal of the spring* (**part k**) *to release the same from its normally radial position.* The spring is removed by means of a single screw (**o**).

30

Early Meisselbach *Featherlight* #280 raised pillar skeleton fly reel which is engraved with the patent of January 14, 1896. Produced from heavy nickel-plated sheet brass with a counter-balance weight opposite the wood winding knob which is mounted into the ventilated spool.

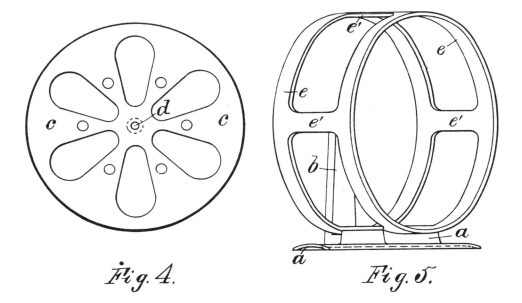

Fig. 4. *Fig. 5.*

Left: Meisselbach *Expert* #19 which derives its design from the 1889 patent illustrated below. The invention consists of a flexible steel frame (figure 5), encircling the edges of the reel spool (figure 4), that can be pressed into contact with the spool to furnish drag. **Right:** Later version of a Meisselbach *Featherlight* exhibiting the same feature (under a patent of 1904).

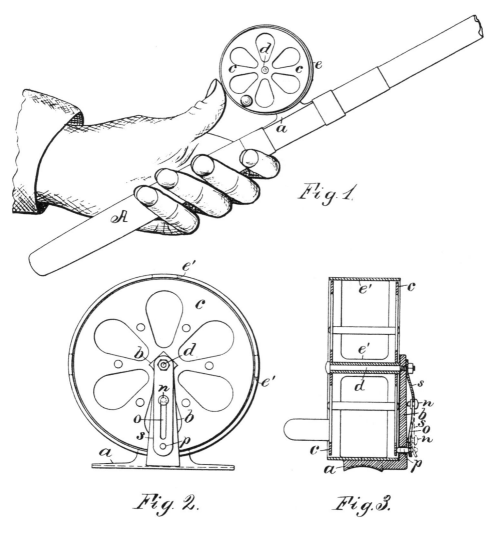

Fig. 1.

Fig. 2.

Fig. 3.

Meisselbach's Expert fly reel as depicted on the first page of their February 5, 1889 patent application. Notice that the reel is mounted in a position on the rod typically reserved for casting models. The drawing serves to portray how anglers were to operate the flexible-rim drag. The reel pictured here is equipped with an *auxiliary braking device* designed to exert a continuous pressure against the spool when engaged by means of a sliding button and leaf spring built into the reel back.

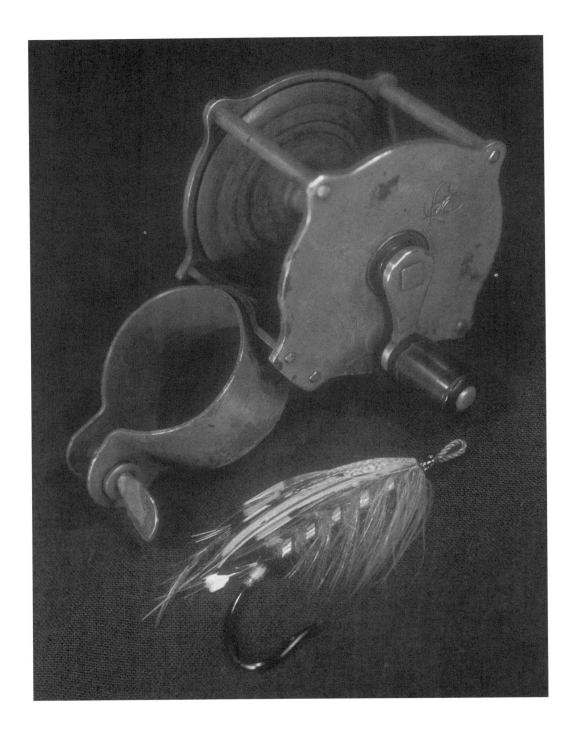

Extraordinary *Abbey & Imbrie* trout reel (c.1890) identified by a distinctive crossed-hooks trade mark. Made of solid brass and fitted with a ring clamp for rod retention.

Top: A group of fishing collectibles including the fairly scarce Four Brothers *Egalite* No. 1905 fly reel sitting upon its original box. **Bottom:** The venerable Pflueger *Progress* — raised pillar, skeleton fly reel stamped with a bull dog trade mark.

Older Pflueger *Sal-Trout* fly reel constructed of brass and set-up with a basic click device for tension. Filled with a modern fly line and ready to go. Despite its lack of a rim control, so popular among the majority of anglers today, this hefty Pflueger can still be useful on the water. Simply regulate drag by placing the index finger of your free hand in-between crossbars and gently against any line remaining on the spool.

South Bend *St. Joe* No. 1170 fly reel similar in appearance to the early Pflueger Progress, brass Sal-Trout, and Shakespeare *Kazoo*. Made of blued steel and fitted with a wood winding knob.

Four Brothers *Delite* single action fly reel made of hard rubber with nickel silver encircling bands for reinforcement. These little trout reels are endowed with a truly classic, traditional appearance found in many of the reproduction models produced today. The Delite and similar Pflueger *Hawkeye* are eagerly collected and difficult to locate in decent condition.

Tiny Winchester *Armax* brand raised pillar trout reel circa 1925.
Made of nickel plated brass and featuring a shapely celluloid winding knob and perforated spool.

Carlton Manufacturing Co. *Lightweight* fly reel made in Rochester, New York. One of the more scarce skeleton types. It is a rather peculiar reel in that the internally mounted spool can be quickly removed as the result of an ingenious pillar to frame connection.

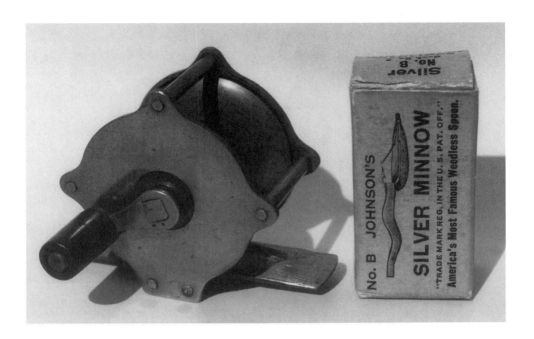

Top: A stout brass raised pillar trout reel attributable to Thomas Chubb circa 1900. **Bottom:** Montague *Waterwitch*, a small multiplying reel that could have been matched with a fly rod.

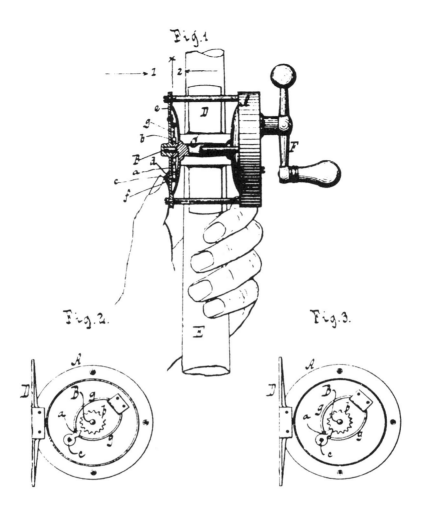

Fig.1

Fig.2.

Fig.3.

The pivotal Edward Vom Hofe 1883 patent for a click tension device consisting of a wire spring, arrow shaped pawl, and operating button mounted on the tail plate — allowing the fisherman to engage it with the thumb of the same hand that holds the rod. **Figure 2** illustrates the off-position click, while **figure 3** represents the device when in gear. Later that same year, Thomas Chubb was also granted a patent that proposed a viable tail plate click mechanism. Comparing the dates of application, it is clear that Vom Hofe filed his papers six months prior to Chubb. And although Julius Vom Hofe (1885), Andrew Hendryx (1892), and the Meisselbachs (1896) would patent similar contrivances — these too were merely modifications of Edward Vom Hofe's original design.

Top: Three Meisselbach fly reels built between 1896 and 1905, all manufactured under the protection of the firm's 1896 patent, a proprietary version of Vom Hofe's famous 1883 click invention. **Bottom:** One of a million unmarked trade reels (left) and a miniature Hendryx multiplying trout reel (right) both circa 1900.

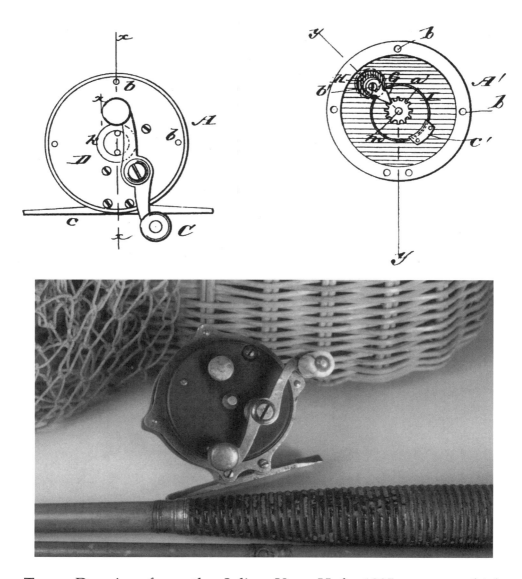

Top: Drawing from the Julius Vom Hofe 1885 patent which describes a reel with . . . *a peculiar attachment of the click, made capable of adjustment so as either to engage the wheel on the spool . . . and indicate by its noise when the spool is being rotated, or to be disengaged therefrom and so permit of the spool being freely rotated and without noise.* Despite the requisite legalese, it can be gleaned from further reading of the patent text that Julius intended to . . . *throw a resistance on the rotating spool.* Thus, another early click drag was created. **Bottom:** Fruit of the inventor's labor — a Julius Vom Hofe multiplying trout reel not unlike the one submitted with his 1885 patent application.

A beautiful Montague trout reel (c.1930) assembled with hard rubber plates supported by nickel-plated crossbars. It is in excellent condition and quite alluring as a fly fishing collectible.

A. WOLLENSAK.
FISHING REEL.
APPLICATION FILED MAR. 9, 1910.

969,235.

Patented Sept. 6, 1910.

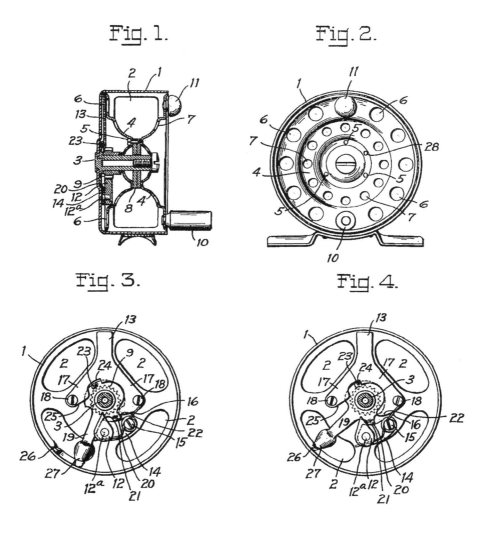

A 1910 patent of Andrew Wollensak which was, not entirely, utilized by the Rochester Reel Company to produce its outstanding Ideal trout and bass fly reels. The internal workings found on most production models consist of a complex arrangement of five layered, integrated parts — all designed to set into motion a lever operated drag with three settings (click, free-spool, and spool tension).

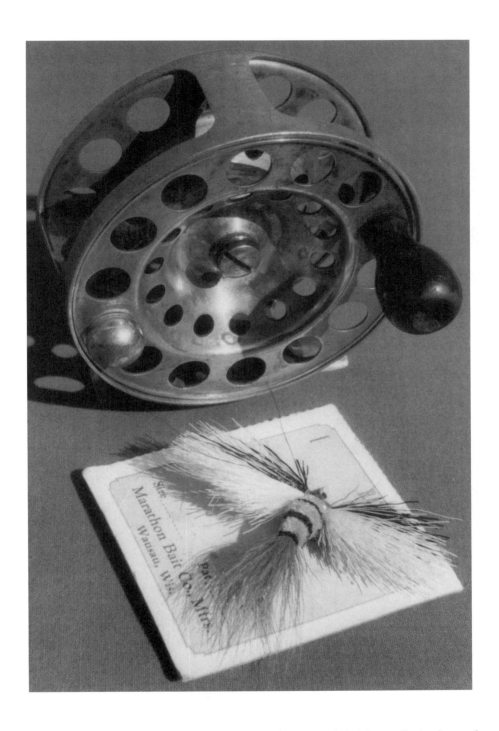

The Rochester *Ideal* No. 2 single action bass reel (120 yard size) made of nickel-silver and engraved with the September 6, 1910 patent. A fine, early fly reel with an elegant wood winding knob.

Four little raised pillar trout fly reels manufactured between 1900 and 1920. All are without provenance except the tiny and less obscure Barney & Berry — from Winchester's factory.

Looking much like a Meisselbach Expert is this wide, large capacity *Hermos Reel* from the 1920s — intended for trolling, but adaptable to fly fishing and probably, at one time, put to use with the long rod.

Chas. H. Kewell of San Francisco, produced the *Kewart* fly reel pictured above. As described in the foregoing chapter, the adjustable drag suffered from an unfortunate defect inherent in its design. Nevertheless, the Kewart is intriguing and is a great reel for collectors to pursue because few are known to exist.

Later American Fly Reels
(1930 - 1975)

A Place To Hold The Line

As a kid, I would often reflect on the sage advice that I absorbed liberally through the avid perusal of outdoor magazines. The monthly words of wisdom soon became my own and it was easy to believe the precepts and doctrines put forth by esteemed writers of the lunker bass or monster trout article.

A favorite notion of generations past was the preposterous falsehood that a fly reel existed primarily as a receptacle for the backing and fly line. Some fishing authors went so far as to claim this was its <u>only</u> purpose. All but the most knowledgeable and keenly astute fly fishers underestimated the usefulness of a well-made single action reel equipped with a functional tension device. Clearly, the lowly fly reel has historically taken a back seat to the fly rod — a piece of fishing tackle perceived to be eminently more significant.

With the onset of tougher fishing conditions and leaner times, trout anglers have developed a delicate approach to fly presentation. In our basic trout fishing, it has become apparent that a smooth reel check is truly a necessity in order to protect light tippets and fine wire hooks. Conversely, the strong and infinitely adjustable drag or anti-reverse mechanism is now a highly desired if not required feature in heavy duty fly reels designed to battle large, "blue water" game fish.

Experienced lure and jig fishermen have always been aware of the advantage gained by utilizing a casting reel with a superior drag system. Since fly fishing has evolved into a more versatile form of angling, which encompasses the pursuit of species erstwhile reserved for the bait caster, quality fly reels now sit at a heightened level of importance. The hundreds of dollars one is inclined to pay for a modern, machined reel bears this out. It is often then for economical reason that collectors seek out old, collectible fly reels for use on the water. Unfortunately, not all classic fly reels from the 1930s, 40s and 50s are up to the task. It seems that mass production and cheap materials often helped perpetuate the "line receptacle myth". In fact, anglers might be prudent to approach the utility value of most old, inexpensive fly reels with trepidation and skepticism.

Notwithstanding their propensity to fall-apart and break-off fish, even those pot-metal darlings of days-gone-by deserve a place on the collector's shelf. After all, pure nostalgia has to count for something! In addition to the "junker" fly reels of this era, a variety of good single action models and a few multipliers were available — ranging from the acceptable to the outstanding.

Sturdy and Available

The most widely used fly reel in history is the **Pflueger** *Medalist*. Although the Medalist first became popular in the 1930s, its unprecedented fame spread from coast to coast shortly after World War Two.

Upon inception, the Medalist displayed beautiful turned pillars and a round metal line guard — complete with a distinctive metal spool release cover. Later Medalists were fitted with straight pillars, a white celluloid spool release cam cover, and square "Diamolite" (chrome plated) line guard.

Very early Medalists can be found with a cast aluminum foot, while the majority are discovered with a chrome foot that is slightly bowed outward from the bottom of the reel frame. It is this uniquely shaped chrome foot which prevents the Medalist from sufficiently attaching to some fly rod reel seats that are equipped with wood inserts and small hoods. In order to properly affix a Medalist to certain modern fly rods, a reel foot conversion kit may have to be purchased. The collector should at least consider any possible modifications required to combine a second-hand Medalist with their favorite fly rod.

When it comes to functional operation, the Pflueger Medalist has always delivered satisfactory performance. A pleasant drag, with adjustment capabilities in every model except the small #1492, makes this a great old reel for modern use. And remember, it is the early "Made in U.S.A." Medalist that collectors look for. Removal of the spool will reveal a durable <u>metal</u> click and drag ratchet attached to the center of the frame. The ratchet has grooves to receive a spring-loaded clicker pawl mounted in the back spool flange. Later models exhibit a plastic ratchet. From the beginning, the Medalist was a great boon to anglers because it was one of the first U.S. fly reels to be marketed with convenient extra spools that were readily available.

In the 1940s Pflueger produced another fly reel, *The Gem*, which was less expensive than the Medalist and lacked the sophisticated drag mechanism of its stable mate. The first model #2094 Gem was set-up with a crescent shaped spool release latch to allow for quick line swaps. Later editions of this reel have a large center-screw which secures the spool in place and is designed with a coin-size slot for easy stream-side maintenance.

Pflueger continued as a major purveyor of economy reels sold under the familiar names of *Sal-Trout* and *Progress*. By the 1950s these reels were quite different than the early brass models of the same name. The new Sal-Trout #1554 and Progress #1774 were composed of a black painted aluminum frame and metallic spool. The spool perforations of the Sal-Trout had a traditional pattern, while the Progress evolved into a symmetrical grouping of round holes. Both models were produced into the 1970s.

One of the most sought-after 1960 to 1970 era Pflueger reels is the *Supreme Fly Reel*. Capitalizing on the name and good reputation of its best bait casting reel, Pflueger created a powerful fly reel equipped with an aggressive drag featuring anti-reverse option and silent operation — in a reasonably priced package complete with vinyl case, lube, wrench and spare parts. The smaller model #577 Supreme is traded at a premium in collectors' circles. Akin to the Supreme was Shakespeare's own heavy duty anti-reverse fly reel (#1898).

Shakespeare of Kalamazoo, Michigan is reputed to have sold over 1000 different casting reel variations starting in 1897. The *Russell* was Shakespeare's main entry into the fly reel market, a typical example being the model #1895 FK (circa 1951). The very first Russell, however, was offered during the 1930 season. It was constructed of a light aluminum alloy with a reversible hardened steel click held in place by bronze springs. Some Russell reels were fitted with a chromium plated line guard. A deluxe model came with a genuine agate guard. The Russell could be quickly taken apart for cleaning and greasing by the removal of a single center thumb screw. In contrast to the Medalist, the Russell was fastened together at pillars and foot by rivets. Shakespeare boasted that the rivets provided "permanent rigidity" and that the Russell was "the greatest trout reel value obtainable". It is debatable whether the rivet system on this series of reels is better than the "screw" construction of the Medalist. Unlike screws, rivets do not fall-out with the vibration of use. Once they break, however, a repair becomes difficult. Screws, on the other hand, may loosen — but they can be tightened or replaced when lost. Essential reel maintenance has always required a quick inspection of any screws after every fishing trip. Unfortunately, not all angling brethren of the past followed this sound practice.

Shakespeare also produced the attractive *AuSable* fly reel which <u>was</u> put together by screws and featured a unique shielded spool design. The Ausable's winding knob is distinctive in that it is molded of a very alluring marbled plastic.

James Heddon Company, celebrated lure maker of Dowagiac, Michigan sold the much ballyhooed *Imperial* #125 fly reel in the 1930s — yet it was the simple *Daisy* #320 model that provided a work horse tool for the average fisherman. The Daisy (circa 1955) had a green enamel finish and was a good, serviceable reel curiously similar in appearance to the first model Hardy Princess. As a matter of reference, be aware that some versions of the Daisy were engraved with the words "Assembled in USA, parts made in Japan".

The Horton Manufacturing Company of Bristol Connecticut distributed the *Meek* series of single action aluminum fly reels under the trade name of the famous brothers who pioneered the development of the Kentucky bait casting reel. Looking curiously like a Hardy Uniqua, the Meek fly reel featured a tool steel click gear and fine bronze spool post (axle) and bushing. This Meek series (#54, 55 and 56), although very collectible, should not be confused with the earlier Meek 44 fly reel produced in extremely limited numbers. Horton also distributed the inexpensive Bristol #65 reel equipped with a metal line guide and astoundingly smooth check.

Meisselbach, a name synonymous with 1890 skeleton style fly reels, continued to be stamped on several trout reels into the early 1930s. These were quality Meisselbach products fabricated through a new entity established by the famous reel inventor, former Meisselbach employee and stockholder, Pliny Catucci. Both the aluminum *Rainbow* and Bakelite *Symploreel* were available during this later time period and beyond — due to remaining stocks sold by many retail stores and mail order houses.

The Rainbow, introduced much earlier than its Bakelite counterpart, was a well-built trout reel vigorously advertised in the 1920s. The spool could be quickly removed by means of a crescent shaped (horseshoe style) release latch similar to the Hardy Uniqua and Sunbeam fitting. Subsequent versions of the Rainbow sported a thumb screw device for releasing spool from reel axle.

The Symploreel offers a silky smooth operation which is unexpected at first blush. Don't let the Bakelite construction fool you — the Symploreel is one of the best kept secrets in reel collecting. This reel, also known as the Meisselbach-Catucci Symploreel, is particularly attractive when found with the optional genuine agate line guard. Although the Symploreel was not perforated, the maker relied upon air vents in the sides and hub as features designed to provide for efficient line drying. A slotted screw facilitated removal of the spool — which held over forty yards of silk fly line (ample to execute the most herculean cast).

It is apparent from references of this sort that most anglers of the past were encouraged to fill their fly reels with fly line alone and neglected use of a braided backing line. Having examined thousands of second hand fly reels, I can attest that backing was not a high priority among average fly casters of the golden age. String, wire, and masking tape were often used as a spool "filler". Fly casters of my generation commonly spliced weak, unwieldy monofilament to the butt end of a good fly line.

A hoard of manufacturers tossed their fly reel offerings into the post 1930 sport fishing boom — at a time when the typical fisherman was in need of practical fishing tools rather than the precision instruments we buy today.

Ocean City, a Pennsylvania reel maker better know for its full catalog of salt water bay reels, produced several trout fly reels including the *X-Pert and Wanita*. The X-Pert can be found with a neat turning line guide and funky drag adjustment device, while the Wanita is about as plain as it gets. Want to collect something even more basic? Keep an eye out for the Ocean City #35 or #36 — perhaps the most frequently found old fly reel at swap meets and garage sales.

Michigan based **Bronson** was responsible for distributing a voluminous array of proprietary and private label bait casting reels.

They made the eminently usable *Royalist* fly reel which seems to be a direct knock-off of Pflueger's Medalist. **South Bend** took a similar path with their *Finalist* fly reel. Bronson also distributed a Bakelite *Take-Apart Trout Reel* that is a close cousin to the aforementioned Meisselbach Symploreel.

Montague Rod and Reel Company, the Massachusetts firm known as a prolific crafter of machine-beveled bamboo rods, cataloged a little trout reel called the *Deerfield* in 1939. The Deerfield is unmistakably a Wanita by Ocean City. A better multiplying trout reel attributed to Montague is the earlier Bakelite and nickel *Waterwitch* — considered by some collectors to be a diminutive bait casting reel rather than a fly reel.

Wright & McGill of Denver, Colorado marketed the Eagle Claw *McGill Autograph* fly reels with a gold enamel exterior finish circa 1960. A drag adjuster mounted on the spool coordinated with a teardrop lever on the frame which alternated tension for either left or right hand retrieve.

A candidate for the strangest fly reel is **Precision-Bilt's** *Mosquito*. A clear plastic winding plate allowed an intimate view of the reel's internal workings. The Mosquito proved to be quite popular until the novelty wore-off. At one point another company, Martin, offered its Precision spinning reel with a transparent gear housing. The design was short lived, so they too must have recognized that most anglers desired complete opacity in a reel.

The Pinnacle of Design

Perhaps one of the finest American made contracted (narrow spool) fly reels can be traced to Floyd Lovens Manufacturing of San Jose, California. Their **Thompson** Model #100 aluminum fly reel is endowed with a smooth ball-bearing check, which appears to be a make-over of the patented British Hardy design. In fact, the exterior of the Thompson is almost identical to the Hardy Perfect reel. Another version of the Thompson had been distributed by Tri-Pak Gun Kit Inc. of San Francisco and was available in a wide spool configuration. It has a black enamel finish and a set-screw to prevent the spool from becoming loose on the reel axle.

A usable fly reel which anglers have always found to be tantalizingly collectible is the scarce **Bushkill** sold by McVickar and Son in the 1950s. The Bushkill was made in a 3 inch trout size and large 4 1/4 inch salmon size with a fully adjustable drag and solid aluminum spool. Both models are driven by ball-bearings which produce a silky smooth operation that is beyond memorable.

And it is no fluke that exceptional hand machined fly reels of only a few decades ago have already become some of our best angling collectibles. A circa 1962 **Bogdan** salmon reel, for example, was designed with both spool and frame machined from solid aluminum bar stock. These reels were gold anodized to prevent corrosion even under salt water conditions and incorporated a retrieve ratio of 2 to 1. The tension device consists of a double brake shoe drag with a range of seven settings from light to heavy. All of these deluxe features paved the way for characteristics we expect as the standard measurement of quality in a fly reel today. Consequently, the most admirable creations of Stan Bogdan, Arthur Walker, Fin-Nor, and Seamaster are near the top of the reel collecting hobby in terms of both desirability and value.

Barney & Berry brand (circa 1935) 2 7/8 inch fly reel — of better quality than it would appear. A very smooth check and practical capacity for a #5 line. Why not use it on a 9 foot trout rod!

Early Pflueger *Medalist* exhibiting turned crossbars (pillars) and a metal spool release cover. The classic round line guide is missing — notice the holes where it has broken-away. Cast aluminum foot is also severed. Due to its various defects, the reel cannot be worth much more than the value of an extra spool.

Transitional model Pflueger *Medalist* No. 1492 fitted with the old style, turned pillars and a square line guide. Spool release cam has a celluloid cover.

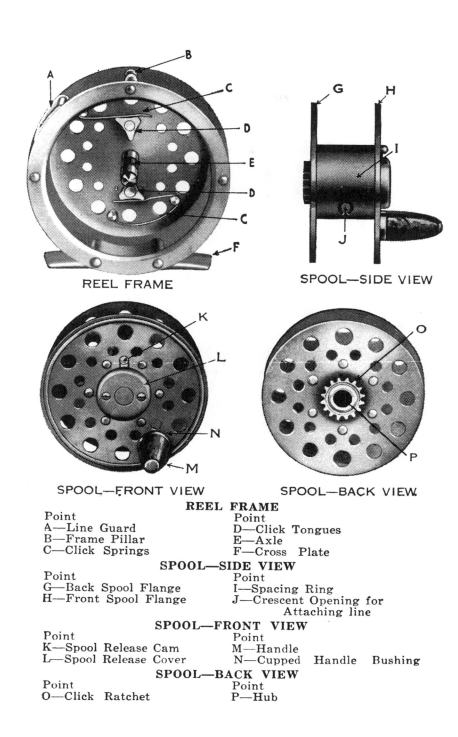

REEL FRAME

SPOOL—SIDE VIEW

SPOOL—FRONT VIEW

SPOOL—BACK VIEW.

REEL FRAME

Point	Point
A—Line Guard	D—Click Tongues
B—Frame Pillar	E—Axle
C—Click Springs	F—Cross Plate

SPOOL—SIDE VIEW

Point	Point
G—Back Spool Flange	I—Spacing Ring
H—Front Spool Flange	J—Crescent Opening for Attaching line

SPOOL—FRONT VIEW

Point	Point
K—Spool Release Cam	M—Handle
L—Spool Release Cover	N—Cupped Handle Bushing

SPOOL—BACK VIEW

Point	Point
O—Click Ratchet	P—Hub

Parts chart for the 1950 **Pflueger Medalist** No. 1492

A quick look inside this *Medalist* No. 1495 uncovers a missing click and drag ratchet, tension adjustment spring, and several screws. Examine any potential purchase for lost or broken parts.

A similar *Medalist* accompanied by all parts in good working order. Newer, machined fly reels are great — yet a used Medalist is still the first choice of many old-timers and is certainly a worthy occupant in any anglers closet as a back-up reel.

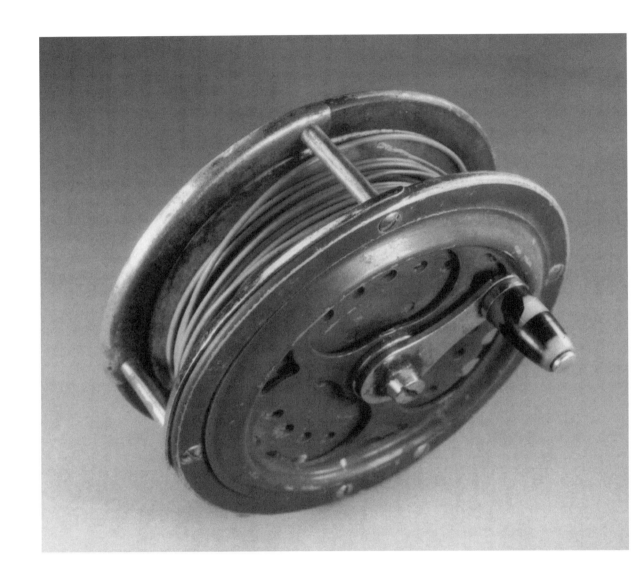

Shakespeare *Russell* #1889 HC (circa 1938). An unusual Russell with a center mounted crank and internal spool. Akin to the Shakespeare *Ausable* fly reel. Fabricated of aluminum and adorned with a charming, mottled winding knob.

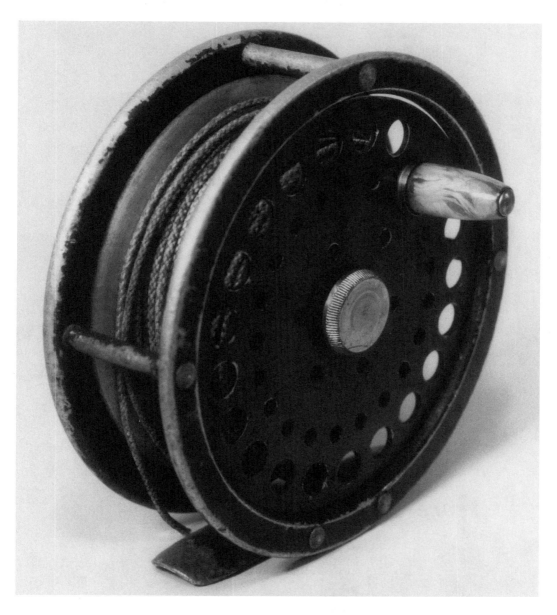

Shakespeare *Russell* No. 1985 Model FK (circa 1951) 3 1/2 inch fly reel measuring to a contracted width of 1 1/8 inch. The cast aluminum frame, outer spool, pillars, and back plate were finished with a medium gray or dull olive paint that is frequently worn-away or chipped. Pillars and foot are riveted on both sides. Non-adjustable check.

Pflueger economy fly reels (circa 1960). On the left is a *Sal-Trout* No. 1554 and at right a *Progress* No. 1774. Both are equipped with a simple, non-adjustable click.

Pflueger *Gem* No. 2094 fly reel — produced with a black enamel finish over cast aluminum. This is the first model Gem as indicated by a crescent spool release latch similar to the early Hardy mechanism. The winding knob is a marbled, caramel color that is very impressive. In terms of collector appeal, the Pflueger Gem may eventually surpass its more common cousin, the Medalist.

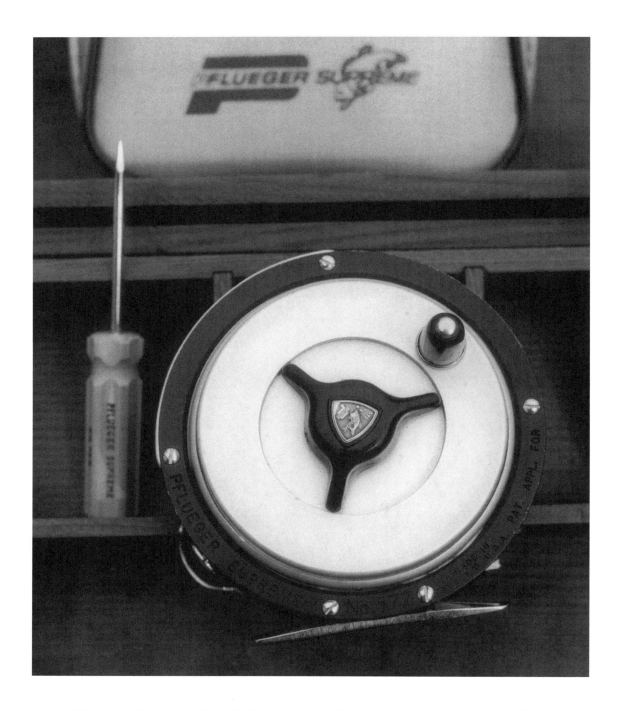

Pflueger *Supreme* No. 577 salt water fly reel with heavy duty drag and optional anti-reverse function. Made in Akron, Ohio circa 1960 to 1970 — packed in a soft vinyl case including lube and screwdriver. Looks like a Medalist on steroids!

Top: Pflueger *Progress* No. 1774 — this one with a counter balance weight mounted on the spool and a thin-waisted knob. Original box circa 1958. **Bottom:** Early example of the Meisselbach *Rainbow* fly reel constructed of thick aluminum alloy and graced with a white Ivoride winding knob. Missing the entire spool release latch device which resembles a horseshoe.

A later version of the Meisselbach aluminum *Rainbow* fly reel can be distinguished from its predecessor — the most glaring difference being a coin slotted screw, rather than a latch, for retaining the spool. Another model, the *Symploreel*, was a Bakelite rendition of the Rainbow. It is apparent that a good deal of thought went into the design of coin slotted reel parts which allowed anglers to utilize pocket change as a convenient on-stream tool. Meisselbach's Featherlight reel featured a spool retention screw that was machined at the bottom of the slot with a depression whereby the coin of choice (a penny works best) could be lodged precisely in place. A subtle yet phenomenal touch of craftsmanship.

About 1935, Union Hardware of Torrington, Connecticut sold the Model No. 7169 pictured above. The spool is concave at the face and displays an interesting perforation pattern. Winding knob appears to be made of genuine ivory.

Heddon *Daisy* #320 single action fly reel assembled in USA (parts made in Japan). A good serviceable reel, similar in appearance to the Hardy Princess of the late 1950s. Notice the two empty holes at top of the frame — it is missing the line guide.

Duncan Briggs Model #2 reel from Providence, Rhode Island. Has a 3 1/4 inch cast aluminum frame. The line "guide" <u>or</u> "guard" (this term is used interchangeably though each word would seem to describe a slightly different function) can be moved to facilitate left or right hand retrieve.

G.W. Gayle and Son Company *Simplicity* No. 6 aluminum trout reel made in Frankfort, Kentucky. Unlike the rare, handmade Gayle bait casters, these mass produced single action reels are fairly common.

A *Bristol* No. 65 fly reel made by the Horton Manufacturing Company of Bristol, Connecticut. It is an inexpensive but reliable trout model made of aluminum and equipped with a steel line guide. Altogether not a bad reel — nice, smooth check.

Floyd T. Lovens Manufacturing Company in San Jose, California produced the *Thompson Reel* based upon a 1937 patent granted to Richard B. Thompson of San Francisco. No doubt, the introduction of this reel caused Hardy Brothers to be distressed rather than flattered — the Thompson exterior configuration mimicked their famous Perfect. Another Thompson, distributed by Tri-Pak Gun Kit Inc., provides a slightly different variation (a black enamel finish and plated retaining screw).

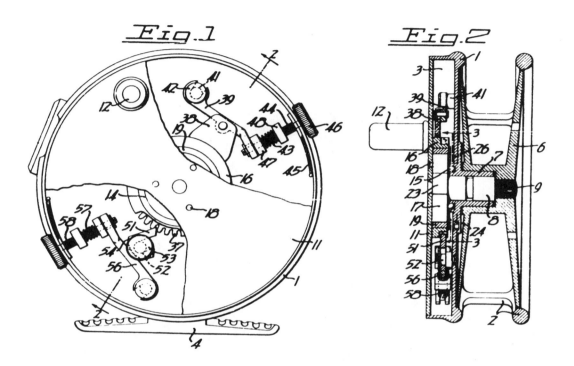

Fig.1   Fig.2

While the cosmetic appearance of his reel certainly parallels the English Perfect, Thompson invented a drag mechanism that is substantially different from the classic Hardy Duplicated Mark II check system. Thompson's drag incorporates a separate brake shoe (**part 38**) for tension and pawl (**part 51**) for click — both mounted upon lever arms fitted to opposite sides of a brake drum (**part 16**). The brake drum is provided with a smooth surface to accommodate the shoe and a toothed area or ratchet for the click pawl. Overall tension can be adjusted in various combinations between the pawl and brake shoe by means of two individual knobs (**part 46**) which each drive a spring loaded stem against their respective lever arm (**part 56 or 39**). A recessed roller cage (**part 19**) houses loosely fitted ball bearings to ease the entire rotation process.

Circa 1965 *McGill Autograph* Model No. 3B single action fly reel with a spool-mounted, knurled "drag" adjuster. A teardrop lever on the reverse alternates tension from left to right hand retrieve. From Eagle Claw (Wright & McGill) of Denver, Colorado.

Lawrence No. 150-R *Sunbeam* fly reel from Lawrence Tackle Manufacturing of New York. A clean, stamped metal trout reel in the original box — still very functional, but not worth a heck of a lot.

Top: Original California *Ross* Model RR 2 (serial number 0635) weighing only 3 3/8 ounces yet capable of stopping a salmon. Features the delightful daisy spool pattern — a collectible of the future? **Bottom:** Ocean City #76 and #35 fly reels from the 1950s.

The tradition of Edward Vom Hofe can be found in Otto Zwarg's Model 300 (2/0 size) salmon fly reel from St. Petersburg, Florida. Dial tension adjuster on tail plate and ornate sliding button click on head plate (face). Silver just glistens and the hard rubber doesn't have a scratch on it — an exceptional level of condition for reels of this type. A superior collectible.

Stan Bogdan Model AF 100 S with silver emblem affixed to back plate (S.E. Bogdan Nashua, New Hampshire). 3 1/2 inches in diameter and 2 inches wide. Made of machined, anodized aluminum with a drag lever on the back plate. This is the incredibly light single action salmon or steelhead style with tremendous line capacity and no anti-reverse — sold by Abercrombie & Fitch circa 1965.

Great Britain
Fly Reels

Winches and Pirns

It is doubtful that we shall ever know the identity of the first angler who crudely strapped a homemade "winder" or winch to the grip-end of a fly rod. Historical documentation and ancient paintings have revealed that the Chinese attached a line take-up mechanism to their boat rods in the 12th century. Early British fishers of the fly, such as the legendary Isaac Walton, fundamentally relied on the procedure of securing strands of horsehair line directly to a top notch or "guide" at the rod tip. No question, use of a reeling device was apparent from writings of the time, yet dependence on such apparatus was not standard practice. By the 18th century, heavy single action winch reels made of wood, iron, or brass were put into service for the taking of trout, salmon, and coarse fish. The first geared multiplying reel is of English origin having been developed about 1780. A rare winch from this era, driven by a 2.75:1 ratio brass and steel gear train, was displayed at the British Engineerium Museum Collection in 1981.

Simple brass and wood crank reels from early 19th century Scotland are called *pirns*. In England, the term *Birmingham* has been used to describe the old reliable bronzed-brass fly reels of that period — in reference to the industrial city where many were made. Superior trout and salmon reels of this vintage came adorned with a hand finished cast foot, ornate crank, and winding knob composed of turned ivory or animal horn. A few exceptional reels were tooled in solid silver. Examples of English trout reels dating from 1850 exhibit spool perforations designed to prevent line rot — a feature thought to have been invented by Americans. The crank reel design eventually gave way to the invention of a knob placed directly upon the spool or reel face.

From 1860 to 1890, several prominent London tackle makers (including Eaton & Deller of Crooked Lane and Farlow of Strand

Street) marketed excellent fly reels of bronze, German silver, and Ebonite (hard rubber). Scots, the likes of Alexander Martin and Robertson of Glasgow, offered fine traditional salmon reels constructed of rosewood and brass. Walnut and mahogany were combined with an imposing brass star or cross back to form the fabulous Nottingham reels — put into use under all types of fishing conditions and now very collectible as decorator items.

Hardy's of Alnwick

In 1872, Messrs. Hardy Brothers started a factory at Alnwick, Northumberland, England. Drawing on previous engineering and gun smithing experience, they shortly developed a very efficient greenheart wood rod-making operation. Subsequently, the incomparability of cane as a rod blank material was recognized. By 1890 Hardy was the largest manufacturer of cane-built rods in the world. In fact, at that time the Northumberland factory maintained a continuous inventory of 10,000 Calcutta bamboo culms. Famous anglers Marston, Kelson, and Halford owned Hardy split-cane rods. Her majesty, The Queen, eventually became a Hardy patron. The notoriety achieved by such endorsements quickly spread, and laid the foundation for what would later be Hardy's most revered product — the fly reel.

Collectors are often surprised to find that Hardy formulated its own composition of metals for reel fabrication. "Hercules" was the patented process metal utilized where conditions demanded high strength rather than light weight. The antique series of *Hercules* fly reels was constructed of this innovative material, know by collectors as bronzed gun metal, which was claimed to be as hard as steel.

Hardy's version of aluminum was half the weight of Hercules metal and bore the trade name "Alumin". On the inside of many early "Alumin" fly reels can be found the initials of the machinist who wrought the frame. Some advanced collectors go so far as to differentiate between Hardy machinists when choosing a reel.

The **Hardy** *Perfect* fly reel, first cataloged in 1891, is the most eagerly collected of all English reels. The first Perfect featured all brass construction with an ivory winding knob, perforated spool, and wire line guard. A simple regulating check with tension screw adjustment and <u>ball bearings</u> made up the internal mechanism. A circular group of steel ball bearings is the consequential engineering feature upon which the reel's reputation for smooth operation has always been based. Another unique design characteristic of the Perfect is its three piece composition — a reel frame including check, perforated line drum (spool), and integrated revolving plate with winding knob. The plate ingeniously unscrews to facilitate removal of the spool.

From 1897 to 1928 the famous Perfect began a metamorphosis which resulted in several variations including a "brass face" model, first "Alumin" construction, silent check, wide spool, and raised pillar *Bougle*.

The Bougle is a Hardy collector's dream that features the "Alumin" frame and pillars (crossbars) cast in one piece. A single, moveable crossbar acts as a line roller-guide. Early examples (circa 1905) display a smooth brass foot and strapped check adjuster. Another type of line guidance system was available in the 1908 *Salmon Perfect*, which was rigged with a special revolving line guard mounted on a brass track to help gain better control when "shooting" a long cast.

About 1917, after having redesigned the Perfect tension check mechanism several times, Hardy began installing a new patented check system referred to as the Duplicated Mark II. A toothed ratchet on the revolving face-plate now engaged an adjustable spring and tongue (pawl) set on posts riveted to the frame. A spare spring and pawl were also mounted to the inner frame. By 1923 the Duplicated

Mark II check was standardized to fit the St. George and Uniqua reels as well.

In 1928 the Perfect took on essentially the same form it was to assume for the next thirty five years. 1928 is a significant date in Hardy chronology, for it was then the company introduced a "grooved" or oft called "ridged" brass reel foot. The proper catalog terminology for the part is a *screw grip palm*. This improved foot was designed to coordinate with the threads of Hardy's patented fly rod reel seat locking sleeve.

Perfects were made available with a beautiful and functional nickel-silver line guard filled with red or gray agate. Often the fragile agate is discovered to be cracked, which can lower the collectible value of the reel. It is important to note that Perfects were also sold with a sturdy steel line guard or none at all. As a matter of durability, it is possible that the no-line-guard version might be the model best suited for modern use.

Post 1966 Perfect reels were produced sporadically and display several cosmetic changes. The exterior finish changed from a deep gun metal color to a metal-flake gray enamel paint. Later, upon reintroduction in 1978, the agate line guard was substituted with a ceramic material. Nevertheless any Perfect, regardless of age, is a remarkable piece of fishing equipment anyone would be proud to own. The great Perfect endured for nearly 100 years and was made in twenty different sizes — accounting for approximately 175 possible variations. What a collection that would be!

The *Saint George* fly reel is another Hardy that is extremely popular with the present day angler-collector. Due to its well perforated spool and relative light weight, the handsome St. George makes for a pretty good balance with modern fly rods. A patented agate line guard graced the frame of every St. George model ranging in size from 2 9/16 to 4 1/4 inches in diameter.

The St. George was initially cataloged in 1911, available in a 3

3/4 inch size only. Two years later a 3 3/8 inch size was introduced, followed in 1920 by a smaller 3 inch trout model. Since the St. George was produced for over seventy years, it becomes necessary for the collector to distinguish between early pre-1950 examples and later versions of the reel. Look closely at the screws that secure the release-latch cover to the center of the spool. Three screws indicate the earlier model, while two screws indicate a later reel. Older reels (circa 1935) will occasionally have a beautiful dark plum finish, highly desired by St. George enthusiasts.

A tiny St. George *Junior* at two and nine-sixteenths inches and a mere three and one-half ounces is the ultimate quest of classic light tackle aficionados. It was advertised to correctly balance with Hardy bamboo rods such as the seven and one-half foot Marvel. Hardy collectors get really excited in the presence of a *Junior*. On the other side of the weight spectrum were two heavy models — the fifteen ounce St. George *Salmon* (c.1920) and the St. George *Multiplier* (c.1930), now hard to find.

Hardy's *Saint John* Reel, brought-out in 1923, upon casual glance looks to be a mirror image of the St. George. A closer inspection will reveal an extra circle of spool perforations and lack of the agate line guard. The St. John is considered to be ideal for light salmon and steelhead fishing due to its large capacity for backing. It was originally made as the personal trout reel of John James Hardy. Many St. Johns are still being used today.

In contrast to the very expensive Perfect and St. George was the basic Hardy fly reel known as *Uniqua*. It was introduced in 1903. The fine Duplicated Mark I and later Mark II check is found inside this spartan, sturdy model.

Dating a Uniqua is easy when examining the spool release latch mechanism. Narrow spool Uniqua reels were set-up with a horseshoe shape silver latch until around 1935, at which time a spring-loaded telephone shape latch was utilized. In the 1950s the telephone style gave way to a cam or "finger" latch. Early Uniqua salmon models had a silver "oval" latch engraved with the word OIL.

The Uniqua was normally sold without a tension adjuster, although examples that were special ordered with the adjuster can be found. As is the case with most Hardy reels, early pre-1930 Uniquas come fitted with a white "Ivoride" winding knob while those made later show a black knob of hard rubber material. The Uniqua, discontinued in 1959, is a super collectible Hardy that will always be a "good antique buy" — reasonably priced when compared to other, more heralded English fly reels.

A favorite of mine is the original Hardy *Sunbeam* trout reel produced from 1924 to 1956. As a result of its unusual cutaway design, the Sunbeam represents an early example of the exposed rim-control drag that is standard issue on most fly reels today. A lovely brass wire line guard surrounds a quarter of the reel and the brass foot or palm is neatly attached to the back frame. Conveniently, the age of a Sunbeam corresponds to a similar spool release latch scenario as outlined for the Uniqua above. Do not confuse the original Sunbeam with another reel called Sunbeam 5/6 to 9/10, which Hardy sold for a short run from 1978 until 1983.

On every Hardy collector's wish list is the exquisite *Barton Dry Fly Reel*. Reliable sources indicate that little more than one hundred of these reels were made over a five year period from 1934 to 1939. The impetus for the design of the 3 inch Barton came from the President of the Flyfishers Club — a gentleman by the name of, you guessed it, Dr. Barton. Outstanding features of this special reel include a broad silver line guard allowing access to the full width of the spool, a ratchet of numerous fine teeth to produce a pleasant "purr", and an offset elongated brass foot. The theory behind the offset foot is sound. When the Barton is combined with down-locking reel seats, it will not project beyond the butt end of the rod —

thus the reel is protected from any blow when the bottom of the rod is set on the ground. The Barton possesses one of the most comfortable, tapered winding knobs imaginable.

Hardy's truly extravagant fly reel was the *Cascapedia*, made of deep black Ebonite and embellished with jewel-like silver components. The Cascapedia was definitely targeted at the affluent U.S. market, in that it is a nearly identical twin of the American made Vom Hofe salmon reel. It was sold in very low quantities between 1932 and 1939.

A fairly young fellow can start feeling like a "gray beard" when the good second-hand reels he bought twenty years ago become collectible. Weird and shocking as it may be, the first issue of Hardy's Lightweight Series is now "recognized" in antique fishing tackle circles. Remember, most of these reels are still appraised at utility value, which can range quite high when the replacement cost of a new reel is considered. Nevertheless, a smart bet is that the *Featherweight*, *LRH*, *Princess*, and others of the series (fitted with a two screw silver line guard circa 1951 to 1965) will appreciate far above replacement cost value. Another quaint variation to search for is the inaugural *Princess* which is distinguished by a pleasant green finish.

The trade name "Lightweight Series", is not to be mixed-up with the narrow spool *Lightweight* trout fly reel produced for a limited duration in the late 1930s with a non-perforated spool.

Finally, a discussion of Hardy fly reels would not be complete without mentioning the *Silex*. These were actually designed to cast and control heavy baits, lures, or floats assisted by an adjustable, integrated free-spool brake. As a result of its outstanding drag, the Silex has been used as a fly reel for Atlantic salmon. Moreover, the reliable Silex has captured a devoted following in British Columbia, where anglers practice specialized big-river drift techniques for steelhead fishing.

Chronology of Hardy Fly Reels

Bronzed Metal	1880 - 1921
All Brass Perfect	1891 - 1900
Bougle	1903 - 1939
Perfect (silent check)	1908 - 1910
Perfect (1912 check)	1912 - 1917
Perfect (MK II check)	1917 - 1966
St. George	1911 - 1983
St. George Jr.	1928 - 1964
Uniqua (MK I check)	1903 - 1920
Uniqua (MK II check)	1921 - 1959
Uniqua Salmon	1909 - 1959
Original Sunbeam	1924 - 1956
Fortuna Fly	1925 - 1939
St. George Multiplier	1928 - 1939
Cascapedia	1932 - 1939
Barton	1934 - 1939
Green Princess	1953 - 1959
Hydra	1958 - 1967
Zenith	1958 - 1980
Gem	1962 - 1969
First Husky	1964 - 1969
Viscount 130 to 150	1969 - 1978

Noble Competitors

J.W. Young & Sons is a prolific British reel maker, albeit some-what in the shadow of Hardy Brothers. The founder of this rep-utable firm, James Young, began apprenticeship with the Allcock company in Redditch, England at the turn of the last century. After the Young business was established as a separate entity, they produced several types of "Aerial" reels for other British tackle sellers in the Redditch area (Allcock, Milwards and Edgar Sealey).

J.W. Young & Sons is undoubtedly best known for their stalwart fly reels made from 1945 forward — branded with the familiar sounding names of Landex, Pridex, Condex, and Beaudex. A great deal of pride fueled the Young enterprise since they were fishing reel specialists. A slogan printed on boxes of the 1950s exclaimed — "Quality, dependability, and our sixty years experience in every model". The most consistent feature on Young fly reels is a generous, dimpled winding knob that feels very comfortable between thumb and index finger.

The most basic Young fly reels were the *Condex* and *Pridex*. Neither was equipped with a tension adjusting mechanism, yet they provided smooth operation at a very reasonable price and were available in several different sizes. A non-perforated spool distinguishes them from more expensive Young reels (exception to this rule is the perforated *Pridex Lightweight*). A durable finger spool-release latch cam functions admirably and the cam cover is emblazoned with the inscription "J.W. Young & Sons Redditch Eng" etched in a circular pattern. These two neat Young reels, especially the 3 inch models, represent one of the best bargains in the second-hand tackle market.

The *Beaudex* was the most popular Young fly reel sold in America. It housed an excellent, adjustable check and was fitted with a strong, rectangular steel line guard set-upon one of the frame pillars with a single screw. The Beaudex is another good buy. Unfortunately its thick, textured exterior enamel finish is often chipped from heavy use. The *Landex* was a big brother to the Beaudex, featuring a larger line capacity and beefier drag — complete with twin winding knobs affixed to a handle mounted dead-center on the spool. Dozens of other, private label reels exist which have been engineered by J.W. Young and Sons. During the 1960s, Young was associated with the Noris Shakespeare Company and turned-out reels under that name as well.

S. Allcock & Co. Ltd., also of Redditch in Worcestershire, is well known to have assembled a tremendous production line of stout hooks snelled to gut for bait fishing. Some of their more elegant salmon and trout hooks were boxed in bulk for fly tying. Allcock also sold a superb cane fly rod called the *Marvel*, along with a reel of the same name — probably designed by neighboring Youngs. Most Allcock fly reels can be recognized by a distinct "stag with antlers" trademark which is sharply engraved into the back of the aluminum frame.

The Allcock *Conquest* is a common fly reel in collections, often encountered in a gun metal or black finish. The Conquest's unique brass spool release "hub" is spring-mounted on the top of the reel axle so that when pushed aside by a thumb or finger, the spool may slide freely off the axle. One Allcock option of the 1930s included a brilliant red agate line guard trimmed in silver. A long, smooth brass foot came as standard equipment.

Charles Farlow & Co. was a purveyor of rods, reels, and colorful flies established in the middle of the 19th century. Many antique brass crank reels, without provenance, are usually attributed to Farlow. Two of the best Farlow fly reels of the 1930 - 1950 era were the ball-bearing Regal and the B.W.P. On the exterior, the *Regal* might qualify as a Hardy <u>Perfect</u> impostor if not for the Farlow name and "Holdfast" trademark etched on the revolving face plate.

For identification purposes, the Farlow "Holdfast" trademark is easy to recognize. It consists of a clenched human fist holding a line or stringer with a slain salmon firmly entangled from caudal fin to maw. Catch and release advocates do not despair — just imagine it was a hatchery fish!

The Farlow *B.W.P.* is now a top collectible in that it has all the right stuff — a red agate line guard, perforated spool, attractive white hard rubber winding knob and least we forget, a terrific drag. About 1970, Farlow offered a reel similar to Hardy's LRH Lightweight called the *Sapphire*. It was available with extra spools.

Ogden Smith of London marketed several exceptional aluminum trout and salmon fly reels. The smaller trout reels were invariably designed with particularly narrow (contracted) spools. The *Whitechuch* trout reel is a good example of what Ogden Smith had to offer the angler of the late 1920s. Ogden Smith fly reels can be found with unusual fittings such as thinly tapered, white hard rubber knobs and ornate, knurled-silver spool retainers.

Alexander Martin and **J. Macpherson** of Scotland gave us a variety of good fly reels in the 1920s and 30s. The *Thistle* series of reels from Alex Martin came endowed with a smooth ball-bearing mechanism and interesting brass spoked-center configuration on the spool drum (in place of a typical spacing ring). No doubt, the spoked-center provided additional ventilation in order to discourage mildew from accumulating on the fly line. *Macpherson* salmon reels were big wide-spool creations with a heavy brass foot and tight check. Both the Martin and MacPherson reels sold retail in the thirty pound price range — at least half the cost of a comparable Hardy. Could the angler of old ignore a wee bit of quality and the Queen's endorsement to save a few quid? Many did.

A Global Market

Over the past fifty years the manufacturing and distribution of fishing reels has become less isolated rather than within the confines of a few nations. Collectible reels hail not only from the United States and Britain, but also Canada, Japan, Argentina, Italy, France, New Zealand, Australia, Switzerland, Germany, and Sweden.

Ab Urfabriken, commonly known as ABU, originated in

Sweden as a watch and clock factory. The company is universally recognized as the producer of the venerable Ambassadeur series of bait casting reels — possibly the best selling reel in history. During the 1960s and 70s, ABU did make several fly reels — the Delta and the Cardinal.

The *Delta* was a bold triangular shaped model that was sold in three sizes. The side of the spool exhibits a raised surface that is exposed to facilitate a finger control "drag". The drag is a disk style combining silent retrieve with a fine click which is engaged as the line is playing out. Fastened to the gray enamel spool-face is a matching triangle winding knob. The bizarre Delta came packaged with extra parts and was imported to the United States by Garcia Corporation.

The little known *Cardinal* fly reel was made in Sweden by ABU for Zebco. ABU applied all of its engineering prowess to this model (i.e. #178 trout size), just as it did in designing the superb Zebco Cardinal spinning reel series. In fact, both Cardinal reel types are fitted with the convenient ABU push-button spool release cam. A sophisticated and unimaginably smooth drag helped create one of the finest over-the-counter fly reels of the time. Some traditional collectors might be repulsed by the integration of plastic parts and a common appearance — yet here lies a true "sleeper" that is sure to appreciate in both monetary and functional value.

And one would be remiss to neglect the collectible potential of fly reels like the dual winding knob *D.A.M.* (Quick of Germany c. 1955), bright aluminum *Thomas Cemm* (British Columbia c. 1950), and deluxe limited edition *EXP* (Daiwa of Japan c. 1975).

Hardy *Perfect* (circa 1935) — an internationally famous fly reel

Hardy *Perfect* 3 3/8 inch size (circa 1959) includes a fantastic soft leather zip case. Features the patented agate line guard, ridged brass foot, and silver check adjuster.

Top: Two wide-spool Hardy fly reels from the 1930s — On left is a *Uniqua* equipped with a telephone spool release latch followed by a *Salmon Perfect*. **Bottom:** Unusual dark black *Perfect* from 1948 made with a steel line guard and brass tension adjuster.

Hardy *Sunbeam* in scarce original box with label intact — a very early example made about 1925 bearing the silver horseshoe or crescent shaped spool release latch.

Hardy first model green *Princess* circa 1955. Unlike the later gray Princess, part of the contemporary "Lightweight Series", this one was fitted with a traditional ridged, brass foot. The odd green color makes this a particularly intriguing collectible fly reel.

Hardy 2 7/8 inch *Uniqua* reel adorned with a telephone style spool release latch. Smaller Uniquas balance extremely well with shorter bamboo trout rods. After a good lubrication, and a bit of tinkering with the check spring, they simply purr.

A typical example of the Hardy Duplicated Mark II check arrangement. The long, adjuster bolt tightens down upon a steel pawl spring that is bent around a fixed post. The pawl pivots on its own post, clicking against a ratchet wheel installed on the spool. A spare spring and pawl are included.

Hardy *St. George* — an older 3 3/4 inch model exhibiting the nickel silver spool release cam cover set in-place by **three screws**. A later style has only two screws installed for this purpose. Notice that the agate line guard is cracked, a glaring defect that will cause a significant reduction in collectible value. However, the crack should not effect the reel's utility.

Hardy *Flyweight* with scarce silent check. Smallest model in the Lightweight series featuring the patented "two screw" line guard (circa 1962). Later Hardy Lightweight type fly reels are designed with a smaller line guard aligned by a single screw.

106

Fine Hardy *Bougle* trout reel constructed of aluminum alloy with cast one piece plate and pillar supports. Features a beautiful white Ivoride winding knob and strapped adjuster button. A very early example of the Bougle circa 1905.

Hardy *Silex* No. 2 (circa 1915). Actually designed to cast heavy natural baits or artificial minnows as a result of its ponderous, revolving spool and integrated brake system. The Silex models are now recognized as potentially good big water salmon fly reels and are employed by Northwesterners who practice a specialized form of drift fishing for steelhead.

One of the most collectible and infrequently encountered Hardy trout reels is *The Barton Dry Fly Reel*. The three inch diameter Barton weighs-in at a hefty 7 3/4 ounces due to an extra-thick rim added for strength and durability. Its line guard is of extremely generous proportions and machined to a very smooth surface for line protection. The unique ridged brass reel foot (saddle) has been produced with ends of unequal length — and a special tapered winding knob beckons any admirer to turn-it.

109

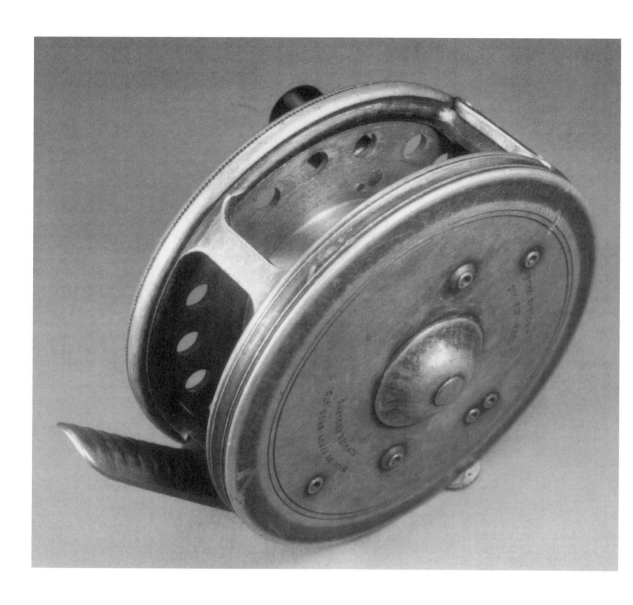

Reverse shot of the Hardy Barton (circa 1934 - 1939). Engraving reads *The Barton Dry Fly Reel*. The elongated portion of the foot is intended to rest at the butt cap end of the fly rod reel seat. A buttery smooth check is just another of many reasons why frenzied Hardy collectors trip over each other when one of these old warriors is made available for sale or trade.

Although not considered to be a true fly reel, this Aerial *Popular* or Trotting reel from S. Allcock & Co. of Redditch, England would provide adequate service. It is composed of aluminum alloy and equipped with a brass foot and brass spokes. The spoked drum is a distinguishing feature of the Aerial reel — a characteristic not unlike the common bicycle wheel.

Black enamel finished aluminum alloy trout fly reel (#7997) similar to the well known *Conquest* model from S. Allcock & Co. Ltd. of Redditch, England circa 1930. A neat three inch jewel complete with deep, ruby-red agate filled line guard encircled in silver. The company's familiar stag trademark appears upon both the box and reel. Includes a smooth brass foot.

Solid brass fly reel with counter-balance handle and cow horn winding knob produced by Allcock about 1900. The foot is thick bronzed
brass and crudely finished from a casting.

J.W. Young & Sons *Pridex* fly reel 3 1/2 inches in diameter. From the incomparable British tackle tooling haven of Redditch, England. The check is composed of a tough single pawl and spring engineered to last. Many circa 1960 Young creations are still in use and will continue to be for years to come.

Ancient handmade brass Lucas & Walsh salmon reel — almost medieval in appearance. Animal horn winding knob and center crank date the reel back to the late Victorian era.

Handsome and early Nottingham style mahogany wood reel from England. The brass-back supporting structure is in the typical configuration of a cross or star. The reel foot or saddle projects directly from the back piece upon which is mounted a click engagement switch.

Largemouth bass enticed by a rabbit-leech and hauled-in with the superb, contemporary Sage 508 fly reel made by Hardy. Any Hardy reel of this caliber is destined to be collectible in the future. Meanwhile it will keep-on crank'in for this angler.

Diminutive, unmarked bronzed-brass pirn with delicately sweeping half-handle crank and a brass winding knob. Of British origin, simple and traditional — absent a check or click. A cool 1890s display piece or paper weight suitable to be located in a place of honor upon any nostalgic fly fisher's desk.

Bright aluminum *Thomas Cemm* steelhead and salmon reel made in Vancouver, British Columbia. A circa 1950 model in the twin-knob, center-pin style. Thomas Cemm also produced a true fly reel similar to the Hardy St. John.

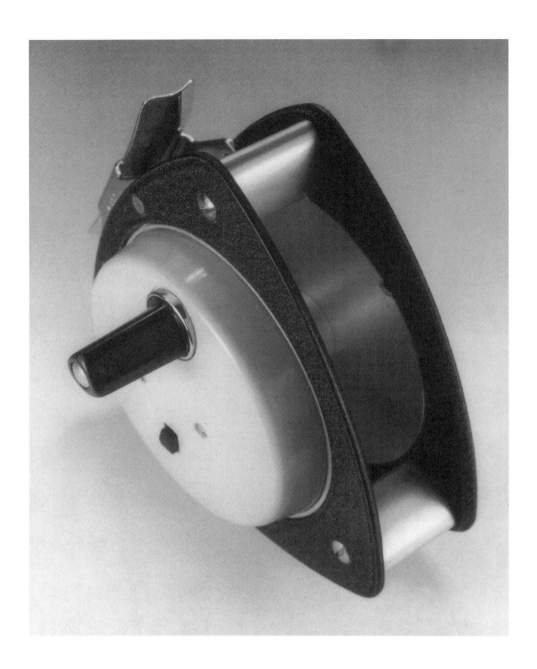

Garcia Corporation was the importer of this bizarre *Delta 3* fly reel made in Sweden by ABU. Features a disk brake with silent retrieve and a fine click when the line is running-out. The light aluminum spool protrudes through a triangular, enameled side-plate to allow finger control drag. Top pillar is 3 3/4 inches from base of the foot (serial #030801).

Large capacity German made fly reel with DAM (#5000) markings and exhibiting dual winding knobs installed upon a highly perforated aluminum spool. Center mounted drag is regulated by a scored silver adjuster fitting.

Sensational, extra-wide-spool Atlantic salmon fly reel distributed by J. Macpherson of Scotland. Accompanied by a charming brown fiber-board box with reinforced metal edges. Perhaps it was an original retail purveyor of the reel who inscribed pertinent information on the box using quill pen. Long ago, for a mere thirty pounds and six, a nattily attired nobleman could have purchased this baby to "chuck and chance it" on the Dee. A collectible four inch aluminum fly reel in mint condition. Equipped with a massive, durable steel line guard and imposing spare spring. Would certainly balance-well seated upon an unwieldy fourteen or fifteen foot spey rod.

Automatic Fly Reels

A Convenient Contraption

While the traditionalist may scoff at the slightest mention of automatic fly reels — a history of our sport would be incomplete and less-colorful without a word on these spring-loaded beasts. And out of respect for our elders, let us give "autos" their just due. Bulky automatics are still the sacred possession of a few crusty old-time bass fishermen who like to retrieve slack line in a hurry. Besides, the automatic allows a person to fly fish one-handed — a necessity for the physically challenged and a convenience for others inclined to do so.

The popularity of automatics has waned, replaced by an almost universal desire for tight and light, machined single action reels. Consequently, there are hoards of old dusty automatics waiting to be collected — from the unusual contraption to the ordinary and functional. All but the earliest models (exhibiting significant patent advancements) are void of any appreciable antique value.

The first commercially produced automatic fly reel was *The Angler's Automatic Reel* produced by Loomis, Plumb & Company of Syracuse, New York. It was introduced shortly after Francis Loomis was granted his patent for the reel on December 7, 1880.

The original *Yawman and Erbe* automatic was sold several years later with a design based on the Loomis patent. Subsequent Yawman and Erbe reels bear the patent dates of February 28, 1888 and June 16, 1891. The 1888 patent is attributed to Phillip H. Yauman (different spelling) of Rochester, New York. Yauman's invention aimed to be an improvement upon the fishing reel described in the 1880 patent of Francis Loomis. The text of Letters Patent No. 378,565 (February 28, 1888) reads as follows:

" . . . objective to make a much more effective and durable reel. The multiplying and planetary gearing employed in the reel shown in said (Loomis) patent is in practice liable to get out of order, the toothed wheels thereof springing or being forced out of mesh by the action of the main spring."

Clearly, Yauman was having problems with defective product returns, and wished to alleviate the nuisance. In later versions, the Yawman & Erbe reel was further improved by the addition of an auxiliary "key wind" which enabled the angler to manually apply more tension instantly. Retrieve tension could also be supplied by drawing more line off the reel so as to wind-up the automatic spring. Thus a "tight line" could be achieved at all times, preventing lost strikes.

About 1915, Horrocks - Ibbotson Company of Utica, New York became the successor to the reel department of Yawman & Erbe. These last Y & E reels are so marked and were produced by H & I for at least twenty more years.

The greatest name in automatic reels is **The Martin Fishing Reel Company** of Mohawk, New York. From his initial base in Ilion, New York, Herman Martin made application for a patent of an automatic fishing reel on May 6, 1891. Patent No. 479,440 was granted on July 26, 1892. Martin provides us with a clue to another motivation for use of the automatic and it is stated concisely in his patent document:

" . . . when the reel is applied to a fishing-rod the winding-wheel is placed between the reel and said rod, thus enabling the fisherman to operate the reel with ease and obviating the liability of injury to the hands (which with the crank-wound reels is sometimes caused by the crank striking the hands)."

Ancient automatics certainly were not "knuckle busters", yet they offered a similar thrill to unwary anglers — a shocking jolt from the rapidly uncoiling spring. Luckily, the spring and gearing was predominantly shielded within a sturdy metal housing so fingers or knuckles were not battered. Traumatized maybe!

The form of antique Martin Automatic most commonly found by collectors was first pictured in Herman Martin's third reel patent of November 30, 1897. Martin had four basic models available in line capacities for species from trout to salmon. The most collectible are stamped with a patent of 1923 or earlier. Incredible numbers of these reels remain in circulation and most work admirably — a wonderful tribute to the Martin automatic's durability.

In the April, 1918 issue of Field and Stream magazine, Martin proclaimed:

"BE PATRIOTIC, EAT FISH AND SAVE MEAT"
Catch your own fish by using a Martin Automatic Reel

This sort of rhetoric might be construed as being politically incorrect today. It does, however, stand as proof of a once abundant and seemingly infinite fish resource. Anglers of the past, with the exception of a very few insightful dudes, could not possibly fathom the idea of dwindling fish numbers — caused both by over-harvest and environmental impact. Ironically, with the current endangered state of our native anadromous fisheries, dedicated anglers and conservationists would better serve the common good by <u>eating meat</u> and releasing their precious, wild catch.

The Martin Reel Company has surely been the driving force behind mass distribution of automatics in the United States. Still there were a handful of other usable automatic fly reels produced between 1907 and 1925. Of these, the Kelso, Meisselbach, and Pflueger reels have the most collectible potential.

The *Kelso Automatic Reel* was produced and distributed by H. J. Frost Company of New York in conjunction with a reel patent of November 19, 1907. All Kelso reels are so marked. A one finger control lever for line take-up and a friction relief mechanism at both ends of the internal spring accounted for the popularity of the Kelso reel. The case and gear housing is composed of a satin finish aluminum which is often dented and discolored from one too many encounters with the bottom of a boat. The *Rochester Automatic Reel* was a close cousin to the Kelso. In fact, many Rochester Reel Company products are marked with an address of 90 Chambers Street, the same location stated in H. J. Frost advertisements.

Another automatic fly reel of the same era is the Carlton brand (made in Rochester, New York to make things more confusing). Automatic fly fishing reels of this nature were rather expensive when compared to a basic single action crank reel — cost of a good auto was three to eight bucks in 1910.

The *Pflueger Superex* No. 775 series is a great addition to any Pflueger reel collection and bears the same 1907 patent date as the Kelso automatic. It was actually produced much later than the patent date would seem to indicate.

A. F. Meisselbach and Brother of New Jersey, through the efforts of their chief reel designer Pliny Cattucci, began distributing an automatic reel circa 1912. Although Cattucci's first automatic patent assigned to Meisselbach was granted June 17, 1913, advertisements from 1912 are plastered with the words "patent pending" — indicating that the reel was on the market between the time a patent application was filed and the date it was officially granted. This heavy "German silver" model was equipped with two revolving rollers (crossbars) to guide the line. The main shaft of the reel was constructed of carbon steel and ran on a set of silver bearings. All working parts were of hard brass and tempered steel. A sturdy reel indeed, which Meisselbach claimed "could be taken apart and

127

put back together <u>by anyone</u> in five minutes". I think not.

It may be true that the "German silver" Meisselbach is one of our better automatic antiquities. Regardless, collectors should take a look at this maker's other nice spring loaded reels — The No. 660 (30 yard size) and No. 665 (50 yard size) *Autofly* reels. Meisselbach Autoflys were produced circa 1930 of aluminum. The Autofly did not have the rolling crossbars of its predecessor, but it did have an improved friction spindle and was considerably lighter. By this time Meisselbach had become a division of General Industries of Elyria, Ohio.

Intriguing and Usable

Is the reader sufficiently impressed with the classic automatic fly reel that he or she might ponder the consequences of locking one of these puppies onto a favorite trout rod? Probably not. Should you be intrigued to the point of action — there are, incidentally, two 1930s automatics that would accommodate a need to experiment. These are listed here as collectible alternatives to the multitude of common South Bends, Perrines, Garcias, and modern Martins readily available and eminently usable.

The **Shakespeare** *Tru-Art* automatic fly reel introduced in 1929, is the smoothest operating reel of this genre. It incorporates a reel brake which automatically releases when a fish strikes — thus tightening the line. The Tru-Art also features a frictionless, chromium plated line guard. This masterpiece of reel engineering came in three sizes and originally sold in the $6.00 range. Shakespeare advertised that the Tru-Art was "Built Like A Watch". And it really was.

From the same era and much more difficult to locate is the **Heddon** *Automatic Free-Stripping Reel*. The reel has a gold finish with engraved white lettering on its face. With the sharp rise in attention now given any Heddon collectible, this reel should eventually appreciate to a value level approaching some of the older automatics.

The quintessential automatic — Martin's early #2 fishing reel.

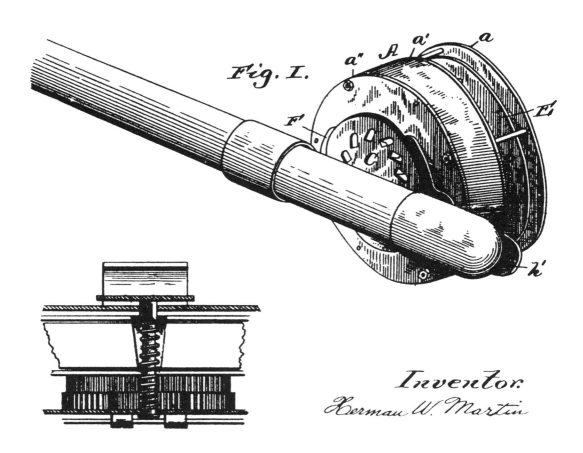

Fig. I.

Inventor.
Herman W. Martin

Herman Martin's patent application art from 1892. A lengthy document outlines the premise and purpose of his invention summarized here . . . *to provide a simple and effective automatic reel by which the tension of the mainspring can be easily varied and regulated by the operator.* The drawing clearly depicts a reel mounted at the butt end of a rod — and from the looks of it, most likely a fly rod.

130

Heddon Free-Stripping automatic reel

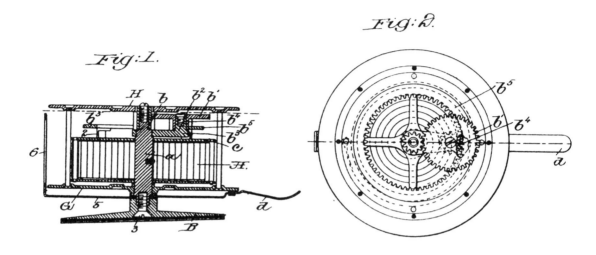

Even before Martin, there was Phillip Yauman (spelled Yawman on the reel). Although Yauman's 1888 patent precedes that of Martin, his reel invention was purely an improvement upon a rudimentary 1880 design of Francis Loomis. The core of Yauman's improved reel consists of a mainspring (**part A**) attached at one end to the reel shaft (**part a**) and at the other end to a frame encasing the spring itself. As line is drawn from the spool (**part G**), a pinion gear (**part b**) meshes with a toothed wheel (**part b-1**) which rotates another gear (**part b-5**) attached to the mainspring frame — thus winding the spring. When the spool is released by an externally protruding lever (**part d**), the spring recoiling effects rotation of the spool in the opposite direction and consequently line retrieval occurs.

A *Yawman & Erbe* automatic reel bearing the 1888 and later 1891 patent dates. This is the second of the early Y & E models, featuring a key wind (missing the key). Made in Rochester, NY.

Pflueger *Superex* No. 775 automatic reel (circa 1920)

Shakespeare *Tru-Art* automatic (circa 1950)

Frost's *Kelso Automatic* from H.J. Frost & Company of New York. Engraved with a November 19, 1907 patent date, the Kelso is almost identical to the Pflueger Superex.

Horrocks-Ibbotson *Utica Automatic Reel* No. 5 in the original box with fish graphics circa 1956. Sure, H & I autos are common. However a reel like this one offers the element of nostalgia — it looks to have sat unopened in a tackle shop for decades.

Oren-O-Matic No. 1125 *Fly Rod Reel* from South Bend Bait Co.

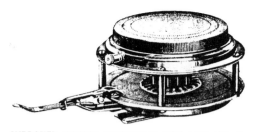

IMPROVED MARTIN AUTOMATIC FISH REEL NO. 4.

Is the largest Reel. When a quantity of line is run out the No. 4 is most desirable as it carries two hundred and twenty-five feet. It has all the good qualities of the smaller Reels besides this greater line capacity. It is strong and reliable and a particularly good Reel for salmon and large fish. Price $5.00.

INSTRUCTIONS.

TYING LINE. Hold the reel in the left hand and the line to be run on in the right. Pass the end of the line through the opening between the outer posts, as shown in cut on opposite page. Loop it around one or two of the six smaller line spool pins placed about the center spindle, cutting the end as closely as possible. DO NOT TIE TO CENTER SPINDLE.

POSITION OF LINE. Where the Reel is used below the hand, the line will come out between the posts as shown in illustration No. 1. If the Reel is above the hand, the line will come out between the posts as shown in illustration No. 2.

WINDING MAIN SPRING. The main spring is wound by turning the drum to the right. If it is desired to have the main spring wound to its full capacity turn the drum until it can be turned no more. This is necessary for winding on at first and for heavy fishing, but for light fishing it is not required.

A few turns only of the drum in ordinary fishing are necessary to sufficiently wind the spring to take up the line in use. It is impossible to state exactly how much line the Reels will take up with one winding of the main spring, as much depends on the size of the line and the amount on the line spool. With the spool well filled, one revolution will take up much more line than if spool is only partly filled, as the circumference is greater. A fair average is seventy-five feet for Reels Nos. 1 and 2 and ninety feet for Reels Nos. 3 and 4.

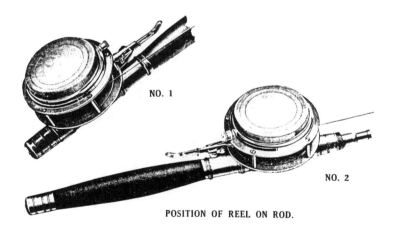

NO. 1

NO. 2

POSITION OF REEL ON ROD.

Page from a 1915 period Martin Reel Co. owner's manual. At their inception automatics were intended to be general use reels. Diagrams 1 and 2 illustrate the versatility of the early Martin automatic seated on either a fly or bait rod handle. In later years the automatic was matched, almost exclusively, with a fly rod.

139

German DAM Trutt-O-Mat #4050 automatic reel

J.C. Higgins (Sears) No. 3152 automatic fishing reel

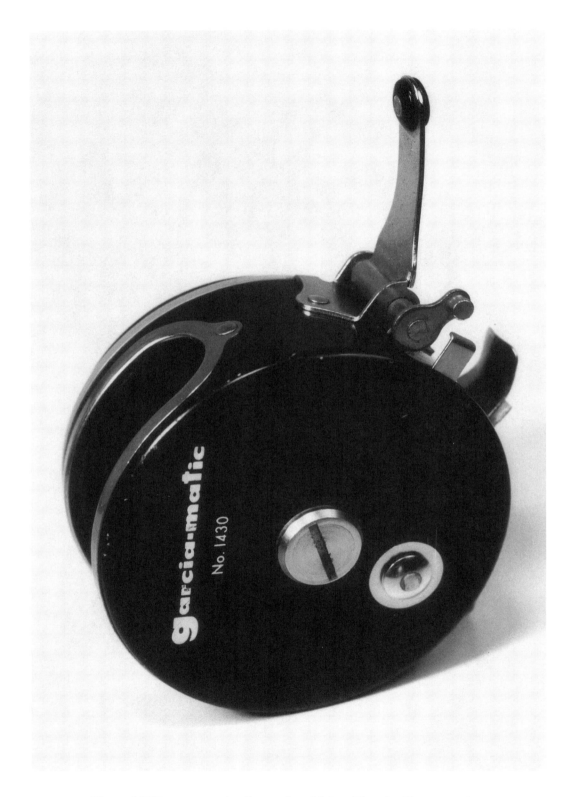

Circa 1970 automatic fly reel sold by Garcia Corporation

Fly Reel Values

ABBEY & IMBRIE

	good	excellent
Perfection brass and nickel trout reel by Hendryx	$35	$60
Salmo fly reel with agate line guard (c.1928)	35	50
Andrew Clerk, N.Y. pre-A&I brass trout reel (c.1860)	300	500
Brass trout reel with ring-clamp (hooks trademark)	145	235
Brass trout reel with pull-up stop latch (c.1895)	125	210
Silver and hard rubber trout reel by Conroy (c.1890)	375	650
Silver and hard rubber 3 inch trout reel (1892 patent)	190	350
Automatic fly reel with line guard (c.1915)	40	80

ABU (Sweden)

	good	excellent
Abu-Delta triangular fly reel (#3-5)	45	80
Cardinal fly reel made for Zebco	35	65

ALLCOCK (England)

	good	excellent
Conquest single action fly reel (stag trademark)	50	85
Black Knight aluminum fly reel	35	60
Gilmore 3 7/16 inch fly reel (J.W. Young maker)	55	95
Marvel 3 inch trout fly reel with line guide	60	100
Marvel 3 3/8 inch trout fly reel with line guide	55	95
Popular narrow spool fly reel	35	60
Trout reel 3 inch with red agate line guide (c.1930)	85	145
Bronze trout fly reel with oval trademark (c.1890)	95	170
Aerial reel of aluminum alloy (c.1925)	165	250
Wood Nottingham with brass star back (c. 1900)	90	140

ARNOLD

	good	excellent
#15 and #18 center crank fly reels (c.1950)	20	40

BALLAN

	good	excellent
Classic raised pillar trout reels (circa 1985)	150	275

BARNEY & BERRY

	good	excellent
Tiny raised pillar nickel plated trout reel (c.1920)	55	95
Black aluminum single action trout reel (2 7/8 inch)	25	40

T.H. BATE

	good	excellent
Small brass trout size reels (c.1865)	575	1000

L. L. BEAN

	good	excellent
Automatic fly reel anodized blue finish (c.1955)	10	20
Single action 3 inch trout reel No. 77 (Bristol)	20	35

BILLINGHURST

	good	excellent
1859 Patent skeleton design antique reel	800	1400

STAN BOGDAN

	good	excellent
Stan Bogdan No. 00 handmade salmon fly reel	900	1500
Stan Bogdan No. 0 handmade salmon fly reel	850	1400
Stan Bogdan No. 1 and No. 2 salt water fly reels	850	1400
S.E. Bogdan Steelhead Model 50 (single action)	900	1500
S.E. Bogdan Salmon-Steelhead Model (AF)100S	900	1500
S.E. Bogdan Salmon multiplier Model (AF)200M	900	1500
Standard Bogdan trout size fly reel (3 1/4 inch)	950	1600
Baby Bogdan trout size fly reel (2 3/4 inch)	950	1600

BRONSON

	good	excellent
Take-apart trout fly reel (Bakelite)	30	50
Take-apart fly reel with agate line guide	35	65
#360 Royal single action fly reel (3 1/2 inch)	18	30
#370 Royalist single action fly reel	18	30

	good	excellent
#380 Multi-Royal fly reel (c.1965)	9	15
#390 Royalmatic automatic fly reel	5	9
Union Jack skeleton fly reel (c.1960)	6	10

CARLTON

	good	excellent
Lightweight quick take-down frame fly reel c.1900	85	135
Skeleton design 2 1/2 inch nickel trout reel	45	75
Automatic fly reel Rochester New York (c.1915)	40	85

CEMM (Canada)

	good	excellent
Aluminum reel w/center operated drag (dual knobs)	40	75
Aluminum steelhead fly reel with check regulator	60	100

THOS. CHUBB

	good	excellent
Heavy brass 2 inch crank reel (Pflueger mfg.)	40	70
Thos. H. Chubb rubber-nickel reel (Vom Hofe mfg)	75	135
Raised pillar nickel-plated brass trout reel (c.1905)	40	70

CONROY

	good	excellent
Thomas J. Conroy Maker N.Y. salmon reel (rubber)	375	700
Conroy, Bissett & Malleson Civil War era brass reels	400	750
Thomas J. Conroy #2 size - rubber & metal trout reel	500	950
Thos. Conroy & J.V.Hofe trout reel (hard rubber)	400	700
Conroy multiplying trout fly reel (all German silver)	900	1600

COZZONE

	good	excellent
Hard rubber and silver trout click reel (c.1930)	125	225

DAIWA (Japan)

	good	excellent
EXP-475 deluxe fly reel (only about 500 made)	200	350

DUNCAN-BRIGGS

	good	excellent
Fly reels of cast aluminum (c. 1950)	10	18

EDWARDS MFG. CO.

	good	excellent
#30 single action trout fly reel (2 7/8 inch)	10	18
#40 single action fly reel (3 3/4 inch) Chicago	10	18

FARLOW (England)

	good	excellent
Ambassador 4 inch salmon fly reel c.1966	45	75
BWP fly reel (c.1930)	135	200
Cobra wide spool salmon fly reel (3 1/2 inch)	50	85
Grenaby trout fly reel (c.1935)	55	90
Grenaby trout fly reel (c. 1966)	35	65
Super Grenaby salmon fly reel (3 7/8 inch)	40	80
Heyworth silent check fly reel (c.1935)	65	100
Kennet fly reel with agate line guard (c.1930)	85	150
President 3 1/2 inch fly reel (c.1966)	45	75
Python fly reel salmon size 4 inch (c.1960)	50	85
Regal ball bearing salmon fly reel (c.1920)	100	175
Sapphire trout fly reel (c.1960)	35	65
Serpent fly reel (c.1965)	40	70
C. Farlow & Co. early brass and hard rubber fly reels	225	390
Bronzed brass trout reel with horn knob (c.1870)	125	195

FIN-NOR

	good	excellent
No. 1 trout or 2 steelhead-salmon fly reels (c.1975)	200	350
No. 3 and 4 anti-reverse salt water reels (c.1975)	225	375
Earlier (wedding cake) style fly reels	475	850

FOLLET

	good	excellent
Bird cage design Civil War era (horizontal style)	750	1200

H.J. FROST

	good	excellent
Kelso heavy automatic fly reel (1907 patent)	35	70

GAYLE

	good	excellent
Gayle Simplicity side mount fly reel (c. 1925)	25	40
Gayle Simplicity #3 fly reel stamped metal (c.1930)	15	30
Gayle Simplicity #6 fly reel with dual knobs (c.1930)	20	35
Gayle Simplicity #5 fly reel (with perforated spool)	15	30

HARDY (England)

	good	excellent
Perfect early 1896 check with brass face or all brass	600	900
Perfect 1896 check, wide spool large diameter	700	1000
Perfect 1906 check with rotating line guard	500	800
Perfect 1912 check with Ivorine handle, brass foot	400	650
Perfect c.1928 - 1955 MK. II check 2 7/8 - 3 1/8 inch	250	375
Perfect fly reel same size with agate line guard	265	385
Perfect 1928 - 1955 MK. II check 3 3/8 inch and larger	200	325
Perfect fly reel same size with agate line guard	210	335
Perfect wide spool salmon fly reel with MK. II check	290	400
Special Perfect 3 1/4 inch with raised face (c.1910)	850	1500
Bougle reel with hand & rod trademark (c. 1910)	1500	2600
Hercules bronze reels with oval trademark (c. 1897)	325	500
St. George pre-1950 (3 screw spool release) 3 inch	285	425
St. George later (2 screw spool release) 3 inch	225	365
St. George Jr. trout reel (early 3 screw) 2 9/16 inch	400	675
St. George Jr. trout fly reel (later 2 screw)	375	550
St. George pre-1950 (3 3/8 and 3 3/4 inch size)	200	325
St. George later 1965 (3 3/8 and 3 3/4 inch size)	175	290
Uniqua 1915 - 1930 (horseshoe style spool latch)	125	200
Uniqua 1930 - 1960 (telephone style spool latch)	95	175
Uniqua small sizes 2 5/8 or 2 7/8 inch	165	245
Uniqua salmon reel 4 inch with OIL style latch	140	220

	good	excellent
Sunbeam trout reel with old MK. II check 2 3/4 inch	110	185
Sunbeam 3 inch with brass line guard (c.1960)	80	140
Sunbeam lightweight with clip-in agate (c.1970)	65	130
St. John salmon fly reel 3 7/8 inch diameter (c.1925)	90	175
St. John modern version (c.1970)	75	135
The Fly Reel with nickel-silver line guard (c.1947)	300	500
Davy fly reel with narrow perforated spool (c.1930)	800	1500
The Barton Dry Fly Reel with off-set foot (c.1935)	1600	2800
Cascapedia Ebonite and silver fly reel (c.1935)	3900	7500
Lightweight early aluminum solid spool (c. 1937)	125	200
Princess first model with green finish	100	185
Flyweight (early pre-1965 with 2 screw line guard)	75	135
Flyweight (same with silent drag)	85	145
Featherweight (2 screw heavy silver line guard)	75	130
LRH Lightweight (2 screw line guard)	75	130
Princess (2 screw line guard)	90	145
St. Aidan large diameter 3 3/4 inch fly reel	90	145
Marquis rim control fly reels (circa 1970 and later)	75	125
Gem fly reels (c. 1965)	40	65
Hydra fly reels (c. 1960)	40	65
Viscount fly reels (i.e. #140, 150)	45	75
Zenith light salmon fly reel	95	170
Husky heavy wide spool salmon fly reel	100	185
Fortuna fly salmon reel w/silent brake (c.1930)	700	1200
The Silex some with jeweled bearing (c.1900)	225	375
Silex #2 with twin ivory knobs (c.1915)	185	295
Silex Major (c.1925)	170	280
Super Silex (c.1930)	290	400

HEDDON

	good	excellent
Imperial #125 single action fly reels	45	80
Daisy #320 fly reel (green) parts made in Japan	18	30

	good	excellent
Mark IV automatic fly reels (c.1960)	4	9
Automatic Free Stripping reel J. Heddon Sons (c.1940)	15	28

ANDREW B. HENDRYX

	good	excellent
Raised pillar brass trout reels (2 to 2 1/2 inch)	20	40
Nickel plated brass trout reels (c.1900)	20	40
Ornate handle style or patented oil cap features	40	70

HERMOS

	good	excellent
Ferris-wheel style trolling or large capacity fly reels	25	45

H & I

	good	excellent
Vernley Bakelite single action fly reel	6	12
National Sportsman Bakelite fly reel	6	12
Sportcraft No. 60 trout fly reel	10	18
Sportcraft No. 100 fly reel (c.1940)	10	18
Mohawk No. 1105, 1106 metal trout fly reels	9	15
Rainbow No. 1107 aluminum trout fly reel	9	15
Utica Horrocks-Ibbotson automatic fly reel	5	9
Yawman & Erbe Horrocks-Ibbotson auto (c.1925)	30	60

J.C. HIGGINS (Sears)

	good	excellent
J. C. Higgins skeleton brass alloy trout fly reel	6	10
J. C. Higgins single action 3 inch trout fly reel	9	18
J. C. Higgins 3 3/8 inch fly reel (by Ocean City)	8	15

HORTON MFG. CO.

	good	excellent
Meek #54 fly reel 3 inch (Hardy style spool cam)	95	175
Meek #55 and #56 reels (similar to Hardy Uniqua)	90	165
Bristol #65, #66 single action fly reel (c.1939)	14	25

JOHNSON

	good	excellent
Magnetic fly reels	25	45

KALAMAZOO

	good	excellent
Empress #1689 fly reel 3 5/8 inch (half-handle)	16	28
Emperor fly reel similar to Shakespeare Russell	16	28
Surprise skeleton style 2 5/8" fly reel	15	25
Wolverine #1695 (Model E) automatic fly reel	6	12
Miracle Silent Automatic #1697 automatic fly reel	6	12

CHAS. KEWELL MFG.

	good	excellent
Kewart quality fly reel made in Calif. (c.1918)	195	350

L & S MFG. CO.

	good	excellent
Vernon Deluxe single action fly reel (line guide)	7	15

LANGLEY

	good	excellent
Langley aluminum single action fly reels (i.e. #175)	9	18

LAWRENCE TACKLE

	good	excellent
Sunbeam #150-R single action fly reel	8	15

LAWSON (Canada)

	good	excellent
Laurentian aluminum single action fly reel	22	40

LEONARD - MILLS

	good	excellent
Philbrook & Payne (pre-1877 Leonard patent)	4500	9000
H.L. Leonard 1st model fly reel (marbled face)	3500	8000
H.L. Leonard 1877 patent (Bi-Metal) trout reel	1500	2800
H. L. Leonard patent #191813 (hard rubber) fly reel	500	850
Leonard-Mills trout reels (German silver & rubber)	450	750
William Mills & Son (Leonard trout and salmon reels)	450	750

	good	excellent
William Mills & Son N.Y. Fairy 2 inch trout reel	650	1100
William Mills Dry Fly light salmon reel	350	650
Leonard-Mills Model 33 Midge reel (c.1925)	400	700
Leonard Model 50 trout reel	375	625
Leonard fly reels (modern c.1984)	250	450
Wm. Mills & Son (Leonard) Gear Reel w/1882 pat.	5000	9500
William Mills salmon reel similar to Hardy (c.1940)	145	250
William Mills Kennet fly reel (similar to Meek #55)	90	165

MALLOCH (Scotland)

	good	excellent
Bronzed brass salmon fly reels circa 1925	100	200
Sun & Planet style fly reels	200	375

ALEX MARTIN (Scotland)

	good	excellent
Thistle 3 inch diameter trout fly reels	125	210
Thistle ball bearing salmon size reels	100	175
Caledonia light weight fly reel	90	165

MARTIN REEL CO.

	good	excellent
Automatic fly reels #1 to #5 (pre - 1925)	15	30
Flywate automatics #27 and 28 (c.1930)	8	15
Flywate fly reel later (c.1950 - 1960)	6	10
Tuffy model upright automatic #81	5	8
Blue Chip automatic #83 and 73 (c.1963)	6	10
Standard automatic #25 (c. 1963)	5	8
Reel-Tuff single action trout fly reel #43	5	10
Single action fly reel #7 dual knobs (c.1960)	5	10

McVICKAR & SON

	good	excellent
Bushkill ball-bearing aluminum 3 inch trout reel	140	240
Bushkill ball-bearing 4 1/4 inch salmon reel (c.1950)	150	250

MEEK

	good	excellent
B.F. Meek #44 fly reel (Kentucky)	6000	10000

MEISSELBACH

	good	excellent
Featherlight #270 skeleton fly reel (1896 pat.)	45	75
Featherlight #280 fly reel	45	75
Featherlight #250 flexible frame fly reel (1904 pat.)	40	65
Featherlight #260 fly reel	40	65
Expert #9 skeleton fly reel (c.1886)	50	85
Expert #11 and #13 skeleton fly reels	50	85
Expert #19 fly reel (1889 patent date)	40	75
Expert #22 large, wide spool skeleton fly reel	40	75
Rainbow fly reel early style spool cam (c.1916)	40	75
Rainbow #627 and #631 single action fly reel	20	38
Symploreel #370, 372 Bakelite trout fly reel	40	70
Symploreel fly reel with genuine agate line guide	45	85
Airex single action trout fly reel (3 1/8 inch)	25	40
Allright nickel plated trout reel with click	60	100
Automatic fly reel (patented 1914) German silver	40	75
Automatic fly reel #665 (c. 1920)	30	60
Automatic #660 Autofly	28	55

MITCHELL (France)

	good	excellent
Garcia-Mitchell #768 fly reel (3 3/8 inch) France	18	38
Garcia-Mitchell #710 automatic fly reel	6	12
Garciamatic No.1430 auto fly reel (c.1960)	6	12

MONTAGUE

	good	excellent
Waterwitch Bakelite trout size multiplier	25	45
Rapidan 3 inch raised pillar skeleton reel	30	50
Bakelite and nickel trout reels (circa 1925)	35	55

OCEAN CITY

	good	excellent
X-pert single action fly reel	12	25
Wanita single action fly reel (c.1935)	7	14
Viscoy 3 inch trout reel (perforated spool)	10	18
#35 and 36 single action click fly reel	8	15
#306 single action fly reel (silent check)	9	16
#45 single action 3 inch trout reel	8	15
#76 and 77 fly reels (line size indicator dial)	12	20
#90 automatic fly reel (manual knobs)	8	15

ORVIS

	good	excellent
1874 patented fly reel (in original walnut box)	1200	2000
1874 fly reel (riveted construction) without wood box	500	900
1874 reel made of aluminum (not typical nickel-brass)	750	1300
Lord I multiplying fly reel, 3 1/2 inch (anti-reverse)	165	250
Lord II multiplying fly reel 3 7/8 inch (Sweden)	185	285
Salt Water Fly Reel 4 inch (similar to Pflueger #578)	75	125
Battenkill early 2 screw line guard (England)	60	100
CFO fly reels made in England circa 1980	55	95
Madison older Medalist style (made in U.S.A)	30	55

P & K MANUFACTURING

	good	excellent
Model 101 single action click fly reel (wire frame)	10	20
Re-Treev-It lever operated automatic fly reel (c.1950)	10	22

R.H. PARK MFG. CO.

	good	excellent
Aluminum single action fly reel (Auburn, WA)	30	50

PENNEL

	good	excellent
Raised pillar trade reel (c.1920) single Ivoride knob	15	30

PERRINE MFG. CO.

	good	excellent
Common automatic fly reels (c.1940-1970)	5	10

PFLUEGER

	good	excellent
Hawkeye single action fly reel (c.1928)	185	325
Golden West fly reel laminated plates (c.1925)	225	375
Portage Atlas (early raised pillar trout reel)	18	35
Four Brothers Delight click trout reel	95	180
Four Brothers Egalite #1905 click trout reel	80	145
Medalist fly reel (c.1930) round line guard	40	75
Medalist #1392 (c.1940) no line guard	20	35
Medalist #1394 (c.1940) no line guard	25	40
Medalist #1492 (c.1940-1970) made in U.S.A.	20	38
Medalist #1494 (c.1940-1970) U.S.A.	30	45
Medalist #1495 (c.1940-1970) U.S.A.	30	45
Medalist #1495 1/2, 1496 1/2 (wide spool) U.S.A.	32	50
Gem #2094 fly reel with early crescent spool latch	25	45
Gem #2094 fly reel with coin slot spool release	20	35
Progress brass fly reel w/bulldog trademark (c.1920)	35	60
Progress #1784 brass fly reel w/nickel plated spool	25	45
Progress #1774 fly reel aluminum (c.1950)	12	20
Trump #576 trout fly reel similar to later Progress	10	18
Sal-Trout early brass with bulldog trademark	35	60
Sal-Trout #1554 aluminum fly reel (c. 1955 - 1970)	12	20
Supreme #577 and #578 fly reel (anti-reverse)	75	125
Superex #775 and #778 auto fly reel (1907 patent)	30	60

PRECISION-BILT

	good	excellent
Mosquito fly reel with transparent gear housing	40	75

QUICK (Germany)

	good	excellent
Automatic fly reel D.A.M. (early)	18	35

#5000 single action fly reel (dual knobs) D.A.M.	25	45

ROCHESTER

	good	excellent
Ideal #1 German silver trout fly reel (1910 pat.)	70	125
Ideal #2 German silver bass fly reel (9-6-10 patent)	70	125
Gem trout fly reels (c.1910)	50	95
Automatic fly reel (c.1910) similar to Kelso	40	80

ROSS

	good	excellent
Early RR 1 and 2 silent drag, daisy spool (California)	110	200

SAGE

	good	excellent
Gold fly reels (504 through 508) made by Hardy	100	190

SCIENTIFIC ANGLERS

	good	excellent
Early System fly reels (similar to Hardy Marquis)	70	120

SEAMASTER

	good	excellent
Handmade fly reels (older model with dual knobs)	900	1600
Mark 2 single action salmon and bonefish size	700	1200
Anti-reverse models	800	1500
Mark 3 (dual mode) large tarpon fly reel	1000	1800
Marlin blue water 4 inch anti-reverse reel (c.1970)	1200	2200

SEARS, ROEBUCK & CO.

	good	excellent
Ted Williams single action fly reel	18	35

SHAKESPEARE

	good	excellent
Ausable #1864 GD fly reel (c.1947)	22	40
Russell single action fly reels (i.e. #1895 Intrinsic)	18	30
Russell #1889 HC reel with center crank (c.1938)	22	40
Burdick trout reel (3 inch) serpent style handle	35	65

	good	excellent
Kazoo single action click fly reel (early c.1920)	28	50
Winner early click trout reel (black finish)	32	60
Sturdy #1861 single action fly reel	12	22
Steelhead-Trout model fly reel (c.1955)	85	145
#1898 fly reel with anti-reverse option (c.1965)	75	135
#1827,1836,1847 automatic fly reels (Tru-Art)	10	20
#1821,1822,1824 automatic fly reels (OK)	8	15

OGDEN SMITH (England)

	good	excellent
Zefer trout fly reels (c.1930) some with ball-bearings	80	145
Whitchurch trout fly reel (silver drag adjuster)	65	110
Salmon fly reels (c.1935)	85	150

SOUTH BEND

	good	excellent
Finalist single action fly reel	10	20
#1110 Oreno Lite single action fly reel (c.1960)	4	7
#1110 Oreno fly reel (older model c.1932)	14	25
#1120 single action fly reel	4	7
#1150 and 1151 marbled Bakelite fly reel (c.1935)	9	15
#1170 St. Joe skeleton design of blued brass (c.1920)	25	45
#1125,1130,1140,1150 Oreno-Matic auto fly reels	5	10

TAHOE

	good	excellent
#201 fly reel 3 inch round line guide (San Jose, CA)	9	18

WM. H. TALBOT

	good	excellent
Ben Hur fly reel (German silver)	2900	5500
Ben Hur fly reel (Aluminum)	1700	3200

THOMPSON REEL

	good	excellent
Single action fly reels (F.T. Lovens - San Jose, Calif.)	250	475
Model #100 dist. by Tri-Pak, San Francisco, Calif.	300	550

UCO

	good	excellent
Spin-Fly Steelhead reel	25	45

UNION HARDWARE

	good	excellent
Model #7169 (2 7/8 inch) fly reel with round line guide	12	22
Inexpensive skeleton trout fly reels (c.1930)	5	10
Automatic fly reels	4	6

EDWARD VOM HOFE

	good	excellent
Perfection Model #360 trout fly reel (1896 patent)	2500	4800
Peerless Model #355 trout fly reel (1883 patent)	2500	4800
Tobique Model #504 salmon fly reel (1896 patent)	1200	1900
Restigouche Model #423 salmon reel (1896 patent)	1000	1700

JULIUS VOM HOFE

	good	excellent
All metal trout reels 1889 patent (star washer on back)	350	600
German silver and hard rubber trout fly reels (c.1890)	250	400

ARTHUR WALKER

	good	excellent
TR-1 midge fly reel	600	900
TR-2 small trout fly reel	550	800
TR-3 trout fly reel	450	700

MONTGOMERY WARDS

	good	excellent
Ward's Hawthorne 3 1/4 inch single action trout reel	10	18
Ward's Sport King 3 inch single action fly reel	8	15
Ward's Sport King #60 automatic fly reel	5	10
Ward's Precision #6784 auto fly reel (c.1938)	5	10
Ward's Precision #6789 fly reel with center crank	7	14

WEBER FLY CO.

	good	excellent
Henshall brown Bakelite fly reel (c.1930)	7	14

	good	excellent
Kalahatch single action trout fly reel (c.1945)	10	20
Futurist Bakelite single action fly reel	10	20

WINCHESTER

	good	excellent
Nickel plated raised pillar trout fly reels	90	145
Aluminum trout fly reel #2730 (3 1/4 inch)	50	95

R.L. WINSTON

	good	excellent
Trout reel in presentation wood case (c.1980)	350	600

WRIGHT & McGILL

	good	excellent
Autograph #3-B fly reel 3 5/8 inch (c.1960)	15	28

YAWMAN & ERBE

	good	excellent
Yawman & Erbe auto. fly reel 1880 patent (no key)	50	85
Yawman & Erbe auto. 1888, 91 patent (key wind)	45	75
Y & E (Horrocks-Ibbotson version) circa 1925	30	60

J.W. YOUNG (England)

	good	excellent
Beaudex fly reels (c.1960 and later)	32	60
Beaudex with rectangular line guide (c.1930-1950)	40	75
Condex fly reels	28	50
Pridex fly reels	28	50
Pridex Lightweight (perforated spool)	30	55
Landex salmon fly reels (twin knobs)	45	85

ZEBCO

	good	excellent
Cardinal fly reel #178 (made by ABU in Sweden)	35	65

OTTO ZWARG

	good	excellent
Silver, aluminum and hard rubber fly reel (#300)	700	1200
Large multiplying salmon fly reels (#400 series)	850	1500

For information on bamboo fly rods please consider:

Antique & Collectible Fishing Rods

Identification & Value Guide by D.B. Homel
ISBN: 1-879522-07-1

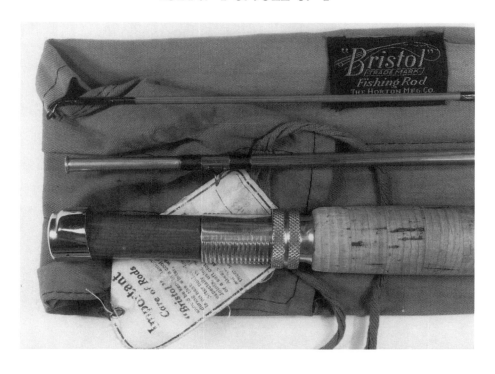

Epilog

In our tackle tinkering and collecting — enjoyable yet often excessive hoarding — it is easy to overlook the recreational and recuperative values of fly fishing. Moreover, one can lose track of the subtler gains brought about by actual time on the water.

Clearly the perceptive skills and heightened sensitivity of a seasoned angler may be put to use in a grander scheme of things. Consider the salient words of George La Branche — who long ago articulated a fly fishing ideal and perhaps the meaning of life itself on a planet where conscious souls are sorely needed.

"No sport affords a greater field for observation and study than fly fishing, and it is the close attention paid to the minor happenings upon the stream that marks the finished angler. The careless angler frequently overlooks incidents, or looks upon them as merely trivial, from which he might learn much if he would but realize their meaning at the time."

The Dry Fly and Fast Water — 1914